YOU AND Y

"The longing grew to have and hold you,
  You, and you only, all life long."

Laurence Hope ("Fate Knows No Tears")

YOU AND YOU ONLY

Angela Hodges

A CIP catalogue record for this book is available from the British Library.

ISBN 978-1-9996978-1-5

Book layout and cover design by Clare Brayshaw

Front cover illustration: *View of the Salak Volcano, Java, from Buitenzorg, Marianne North Gallery, Royal Botanic Gardens, Kew* (Wikimedia Commons)

Prepared and printed by:

York Publishing Services Ltd
64 Hallfield Road
Layerthorpe
York YO31 7ZQ

Tel: 01904 431213

Website: www.yps-publishing.co.uk

For Mac and Flo

With much gratitude for all their help to:

The Chave family – particularly Thomas Bailey and Sally McLean, Will Barber Taylor, Phil Hodges, Carol Parker, Dawn Robson, Lizzie White, Sue Moore, Mary Graham, Julie Neale, Elizabeth Semper O'Keefe, Stuart Webb, Laura Housden of Cambridgeshire Archives, Rhys Griffiths from Herefordshire Archives and Records Centre, Bowden Preparatory School at Altrincham.

Miss Florence Chave's diary 1897-98 is held with the Chave family papers in the Herefordshire Archives and Records Centre.

Edited and published 2022 by Angela Hodges

ISBN 978-1-9996978-2-2

Contents

PART 1 – MISSING
1972

Basement Flat
Albert House
Portland Street
Hereford

Friday 5th May 1972

Mr Hugh O'Donnell
c/o Indonesia Hotel
Jakarta

Dear Hugh

I'm so worried – I can't eat or sleep. I miss you every second. I've had no letter from you since the day you got there. I don't know if you've had an accident or if you're ill. And mixed up with this awful worry is the feeling of guilt. If only I had gone with you. If only I hadn't chickened out at the last minute. I'd be there with you, looking after you, or at any rate knowing what's happening.

I don't know who to ask. I could contact Maria, but I don't know if you told her about us before you left, and if you didn't and everything is really alright – if your letters have just got lost somewhere – that would be an awful way for her find out.

I keep wondering if you found the sacred elephant cave you were looking for. I have been sewing an elephant. Sewing keeps my mind off things, and it gives me a warm feeling when I think about how you liked – like – my elephants. This one is for Alice – Giles' daughter. Mum sighed when I told her. Mum doesn't approve of my elephants. She thinks it's something I ought to have grown out of. She says sewing makes her feel like throwing a brick through a window. She thinks I'm a changeling. I sometimes wonder if I am too. They're all so adventurous – Mum and Dad and Rob – always off on some challenge or other – and I just stay at home in my little bedsit and sew. If I'd been like them, I would have said "yes" to you like a shot, wouldn't I?

I wish I had. If only I had.

Please write. Please.

Jane

The Basement Flat
Albert House
Portland Street
Hereford

Saturday 6th May 1972

Mr Hugh O'Donnell
c/o Indonesia Hotel
Jakarta

Darling Hugh

Just before I drop your letter into the post box at the end of Portland Street, I kiss the place where I hope against hope that you will open it. And then it's gone. Another one into a black hole.

I wonder what the staff at the Hotel do with my letters. Are they piling up in some pigeon hole? Are they thrown away? I just had an awful thought – perhaps you have had an accident and Maria has asked them to send any mail on to her! It's crazy that I can't find out what's happened.

I think I will stop writing. But if I do, it's like giving up on you. This is awful. Where are you?

Love

Jane

The Basement Flat
Albert House
Portland Street
Hereford

Sunday 7th May 1972

Mr Hugh O'Donnell
c/o Indonesia Hotel
Jakarta

Darling Hugh

This is the last letter I am going to write to you until you come home to me. Not writing to you every day feels like giving up on you but I don't know what is happening to my letters.

Look after yourself.

Remember how much I love you.

Your Jane

JANE'S DIARY

Monday night 8th May 1972

I am not writing any more letters to Hugh. If something has happened to him, then he is not getting them, and if he is ignoring me, then it's humiliating to keep on writing – but I don't believe for a second that he's ignoring me. Anyway, instead of writing to him, I am going to write a diary. I'm reading one at work at the moment. Giles is dealing with the sale of the Moor House and has asked me to look through some of Miss Chave's papers. I found this fascinating Victorian diary amongst them. It's written in an exercise book and only covers one year – 1897 to 1898. I have decided to read one page of Miss Chave's diary each day, and write one page of mine each night. Her diary and mine will walk together until hers finishes, and then mine will finish too, because Hugh will be home safe and everything will be like it was before. It will be like a charm. If I believe it, it will happen.

Before I went to sleep, I read again, for the hundredth time, Hugh's last letter. He says he loves me and misses me and he's going to come home and sort me out. That's rather sexy. I woke up in my lumpy sofa-bed this morning and my legs went all fizzy with thinking about it happening. Then I remembered that his letters have stopped. You think everything is normal and then the realisation hits you on the head, bang!

At least at work the constant question whirling around inside my head stops because I have to concentrate. I'm lucky that Giles gave me the job of sorting out Miss Chave's stuff. It was only because he knows I volunteer at the Record Office sometimes. He seems to think I will be knowledgeable enough to work out what Miss Jancey will want and what can be thrown out. I have had it all moved from Moor House to the office in St Owen Street. I asked Giles if I could store them in the little room at the top of the house. He grumbled a bit because there were over a thousand Victorian glass plate negatives among Miss Chave's things and they had to be lugged up three sets of stairs.

When I first saw those, I thought how Hugh would have liked to have had a look at them. For the last twelve months I have thought of nothing without connecting it in some way to Hugh. Each time I do it now, I get a jolt of pain. When I see those negatives, I think of him leaving for Java with his camera in its scruffy old case slung over his shoulder. I have to imagine it because I never saw it. Just as I never saw the look on his face when he opened my note, but it makes my heart ache now to imagine it.

I won't sleep if I think of that, so I am going to remember instead how he lifted me up so that I could scramble onto the plinth of George Cornewall Lewis outside Shire Hall, and insisted I balance there while he took my photograph.

Tuesday 9th May 1972

Nothing from Hugh.

Still working on Miss Chave's papers. She was about 30 when she wrote her diary, and she lived until she was 104. I found a newspaper article about her when she was celebrating her 100th birthday. She never married, and she doesn't seem to have minded being the daughter to stay at home and look after her parents. Fancy living in the same house your entire life! I feel rather envious. With Dad in the army, I've never really had a home.

I wonder if that is part of the reason why I was scared of going to Java with Hugh. All my life I have been moved from one place to another with no say in what happens to me. I just want to stay put. Actually, I think I'm kidding myself. It wasn't so much going to Java – it was committing myself to Hugh.

His last letter was so loving. It makes me certain that there's no way he would suddenly decide he's had enough of me and just stop writing. But the alternative is that something has happened to him. Perhaps he got lost trying to find that cave.

Perhaps Miss Chave was right not to have a man in her life.

Wednesday 10th May 1972

I dreamt last night Hugh was high up in some wild place in Java, all alone. He was cold and frightened. It was awful. I went for a run before work to clear my mind. Hugh would pull my leg about that. I'm not the athletic type. But it did make me feel better.

And it was a relief to get to work and climb up those narrow, creaky stairs to the low-ceilinged room where Miss Chave's boxes are. You can't hear the traffic up there. There's just the sound of the odd fly thudding softly against the dusty little sash window. I stood there for a bit before I started work, looking at the Cathedral spire. Hugh and I sat in the Cathedral once. He told me it was legal to shoot Welshmen in the Cathedral close with a longbow, and wasn't I glad he was Irish? There was a visiting choir practising and we sat at the back and listened. We were so at peace with each other that there was no need for words. Our minds felt as close as two minds could be in separate bodies.

There were no family photo albums in the Moor House attic. Perhaps Miss Chave left them to the family in her will or something. Apparently she had family in Australia. There was just one photo in a frame of the whole family. They aren't smiling, but then they didn't in those days in case people thought they were loopy. I worked it out that it must have been taken in the late 1880s because Flo Chave looks to be about 20. She is not exactly beautiful but there is a serenity about her. She has a nice face. Her father has intelligent, lively eyes and a big white beard, and her mother looks comfortable. There are three brothers and three sisters, including Flo. It was taken near the front door of the Moor House.

It's rather a sensible looking house, a bit like Miss Chave. From the newspaper report (and from her diary too), she sounds like a calm, practical sort of a person. I wonder if people grow to be like their houses – as they're supposed to come to resemble their dogs. I hope not. My basement bedsit doesn't have a nice character at all. The only thing I like about it is the doorbell. The house is divided into three flats with a doorbell for each at the front door. If you press them one after another, you get "ting", "ting", "squirp", and the squirp sound is mine. It makes me smile when I hear it.

I love Hugh's flat in Cantilupe Street. The house is on a corner and seems to be looking both ways, all windows and angles and interesting brick patterns. It always seems to be more Hugh's than Maria's. There is nothing of Maria there – only her black and white photographs on the walls. I love the way the Victorians had time and imagination to add twirly bits to their houses. Perhaps I will never go to Hugh's flat again. I can't bear it.

Thursday 11ᵗʰ May 1972

I was watching the local news this morning before work, not really listening properly, when the newsreader said, "Hugh O'Donnell – better known to readers of the *Daily Sketch*, as the cartoonist, 'HOD', has gone missing while on a walking trip in Indonesia. O'Donnell is the creator of the cartoon, 'Klambi, the Invisible Elephant'. My hand jumped so that half my cornflakes scattered over the floor.

Hugh's dear, familiar face was on the screen, the eyes drooping slightly at the outer edges, his curly hair a little grey at the temples, and his mouth half smiling as if he was just beginning to get a joke.

Maria was being interviewed. She said she had got worried after hearing nothing from him. She had been in touch with the authorities in Java and they were initiating a search. I can't believe I wouldn't know if he were dead. But that dream – is he hurt? Lying somewhere?

Giles appeared in the doorway of my little attic room today. I was sitting on the floor, staring into space.

"So here you are!"

"You did ask me to sort out Miss Chave's effects."

"I didn't think you were going to spend the rest of your working life doing it. I need my secretary back."

"But I haven't finished yet."

"You won't finish it sitting there dreaming, will you?"

Then he suddenly said, "Are you alright?" And I had to say I was, but I'm not.

As I was walking home after work, it occurred to me that perhaps Maria didn't know about the sacred elephant cave Hugh was trying to find. But she must do! I'm sure she must.

Friday 12th May 1972

No letter. Nothing on the news. I feel so helpless. I climb the stairs to look through Flo's boxes and try to forget.

Flo Chave seems to be a very go-ahead sort of a girl. She cycles 24 miles in a day. The 1890s was a boom time for cycling. I remember Miss Jancey telling me about it. Everybody who could afford it had a bicycle. Women would get turned out of a restaurant if they were wearing trousers so they used strange devices to hoick their skirts up while cycling and let them down again when they had to be demure.

The glass plate negatives appear to belong to a man called Dr W A McCutchan. There's a trunk with his name on it, with foreign labels, and inside there are heaps of medical books and papers. I wonder what connection he had with the family.

I don't know what I would have done without Flo's boxes the last few days.

Jeanie caught me staring out of the office window this morning and suddenly said,

"Have you broken up with that man you were going out with?"

And I just broke down and cried on her shoulder. I never realised what a kind person she is. I've never felt able to talk to her about Hugh before because I thought she would disapprove of my going out with a married man. She said all sorts of comforting things about Hugh's situation, none of which I believed.

LETTER FROM HUGH TO
JANE MACDONALD

Hotel Indonesia, Jakarta

1ˢᵗ May 1972

Darling Jane

Tomorrow, I am leaving for Klambi's sacred elephant cave, and travelling through an area where there are no settlements at all. It's pretty wild. I'll be fine. I don't want you to worry, but I couldn't go without telling you that before I left, I talked to Maria about us.

I knew she would be alright about it but I hadn't realised that she had been waiting for me to tell her for ages! She said she knew there was someone and she was pleased for me – relieved, I think, because apart from anything else we haven't had sex for years and she felt guilty that she was depriving me! I told her that actually you and I weren't lovers in that sense and she said, "Well, why the hell don't you get on with it?"

In your last letter, you told me you loved me and you were sorry you hadn't come with me. It was my fault, sweetheart. I shouldn't have rushed you. "Come to Java with me," I said – prize eejit that I am! "Come to Java and when we get back, we'll get married." I didn't even ask you, for mercy's sake!

I know I'm a bit of a liability. I'm a lot older than you and I've no common sense at all, not to mention being married, but you know that my marriage to Maria has not really been a marriage for a long time now – just a very good friendship. I was too young when I married her, and she knew it. She has always said my freedom is there if I want it. Until now, I have never had the desire to take it, but now I know that I want to spend my life with you. My heart is in you, mavourneen.

1000 miles away but utterly yours, now and always

Hugh

JANE'S DIARY

Saturday 13th May 1972

A letter – at last! I am desperate to write back but I mustn't. The charm won't work if I break the rules. And, anyway, it was written before he went missing so I probably still wouldn't get a reply. I don't feel so bad now about letting him down at the last minute. And it's such a relief to know that he has spoken to Maria about me. If the worst happens and he never comes back, at least I know that we would have been married.

And if, as he says, he is travelling through an area where there are no settlements, then perhaps he is just out of contact. It would be like him not to tell the hotel that he is going to be away for a while. A month though! I keep wondering if he told Maria where he was going.

Flo Chave has written in her diary that someone has sent her a gift of flowers. Perhaps she has a man in her life after all.

Mr H O'Donnell
c/o Hotel Indonesia
Jakarta

My Darling Hugh

I don't know if or when you will get this but I just had to write.

Your letter of 1st May has just arrived. I think it must have come via the moon.

Darling, it wasn't your fault that I didn't go to Java with you or agree to get married. It was mine. And it wasn't that I didn't love you or trust you enough to want to spend the rest of my life with you – it was myself I didn't have confidence in. You are so intelligent (no, you are!) and wise and you don't give a damn what anybody thinks about you, and I feel that next to you I know nothing, and I care desperately what people think about me. It wasn't that I was afraid of the idea of spending the rest of my life with you – it was that I was afraid of living beside you in the outside world.

But your letter makes me realise that nothing, nothing matters except that we feel the same about each other, and I will happily, very happily be yours for ever.

Love

Your Jane

JANE'S DIARY

Sunday 14th May 1972

I have written to Hugh. I thought, as he has told Maria about us, it wouldn't matter if it got sent to her. I couldn't bear not to reply to his letter, but now I wish I hadn't. I think I've spoilt everything. The charm won't work.

I was imagining today what it would be like to live to be 104 like Flo. If Hugh doesn't come back, I will have years and years and years without him. I may get so old that he will be like a tantalising childhood memory that I can't quite catch hold of. I was remembering one August evening lying on a hill together – feeling the curve of his body behind me, the happy buzz of insects and the roughness of the rug on my cheek. Perhaps one day I will still be able to remember all that, but will I be able to remember how it made me feel inside?

Saturday 27th May 1972

I haven't been writing in my diary lately. I told myself the charm idea was stupid, and anyway I had messed it up by writing that letter, but today everything changed. I went to see Maria. If only I had done it before.

Ever since I found out that Hugh had spoken to her about us, I had been steeling myself to go. I had this feeling that she might not know where he was heading for when he went missing. Being stupid, cowardly me, though, I kidded myself that she did, and I put it off.

It was Flo who made it happen. I had been reading about Flo cycling everywhere back in the 1890s, and Giles gave me his mother's old bike so that I could ride in her tyre tread, so to speak. I went up and down Giles' driveway till I felt confident and then ventured out onto

Broomy Hill. I was pretty sure Giles stayed at the top of the drive, watching anxiously until I was out of sight.

I had a bittersweet afternoon, visiting all the places which had special memories of Hugh. As I was on my way home, I had to pass Maria's photographic studio in Offa Street. A plan flashed into my head to go in and talk to her, but at the last minute as I was drawing level to her studio, I felt I couldn't do it. Just then the van in front of me braked suddenly. In a panic, I grabbed at the back brake – went over backwards and collapsed in a heap in the road. The van went on without seeing, but Maria leapt out of her studio and insisted on giving me a cup of tea. She is not the sort of person you say no to. I can understand how Hugh found himself married to her aged 20.

Once I was actually in there, I didn't feel so scared. It was a bit like jumping into the deep end of a swimming pool. After you're in the water, it's never quite as scary as it was standing on the edge worrying about it. While Maria was out the back making me the tea, I decided I was going to tell her who I was, and ask her if she knew about Hugh's cave.

There was a photo of Hugh on the wall. When she came back with the tea, I said, "That's Hugh O'Donnell who's missing," and she said yes, it was, and that he was her husband. I asked if she had any idea where he might be, and she said no. I took a deep breath and said,

"He told me he was going to find a cave – a sacred elephant cave."

She looked me right in the eye and I could see that she knew who I was, and she said, "You're Jane! Of course – you're Jane!" But then what I had just told her seemed to register with her suddenly.

"What elephant cave?"

She hadn't known.

And if I had only had the courage to go and see her before, the authorities would have known where to look for Hugh right from the start. Apparently, he had hired a guide but hadn't told the people at the hotel where they were going.

She said I must come again and we would talk, but now she had to ring the Foreign Office and let them know, so I gulped down my sweet tea and left.

I've spent my whole life telling myself that nothing really matters. If it doesn't matter, it can't hurt you. But Hugh does matter. It's so scary that finally something in my life really matters. And when you love someone, you've got to act. You can't just sit back and let others do it for you. Even if you make a mistake or get into trouble, you've got to act.

Monday 29th May 1972

I rang Maria from work today and gave her my office telephone number in case there should be any news. She said the Foreign Office was going to get on to the authorities in Java and ask them to search the area Hugh was aiming for. She was terrifically excited and hopeful. It made me feel a lot better, and less guilty about not going to her right away. She said I could come over any time if I wanted to talk.

I went to British Home Stores after work to buy two fish fingers and 2 oz of frozen peas for my Friday night dinner – it's the end of the month and I'm broke. Anyway, there was a little old lady at the head of the queue in BHS. Behind her was a woman with a child in a pushchair and then me. The poor old lady was having trouble with the new decimal coins. The girl on the till was looking bored and not being very helpful, and the woman with the pushchair was sighing impatiently.

My instinct was to help but as usual I started to overthink it. Would the old lady's pride be hurt? Would the woman in front think I was trying to show her up? While I was dithering, I remembered my new resolution – to ACT no matter what. I found myself walking up to the counter and helping the old lady to pay. She didn't mind at all. I could see the relief on her face. As she walked away, the woman with the pushchair suddenly smiled and gestured me to go in front of her. I had been dreading the weekend ahead but that little incident made me feel better.

Sometimes I don't see anyone at all from Friday to Monday. I know I could go out for a walk but seeing other people all WITH someone makes me feel even more lonely. I know I'm pathetic.

Well, I suppose there are always elephants. Strange that elephants have played such a big part in my life, even falling in love with someone who makes his living out of one.

Thursday 1ˢᵗ June 1972

I went into the library at lunchtime to see if they had any maps of Java. They showed me what they had but I couldn't find any mention of the cave. As I went downstairs, I thought – this is crazy! Maria has been in touch with the authorities over there as well as the Foreign Office – she has got to know SOMETHING about the situation over there! Talking to her has to be better than wandering around in this total cloud of ignorance. Act! I thought. Act!

There would just be time to go round to the studio before I had to be back at work. As I was rushing towards the library exit, I nearly flattened the decimal coin lady I had rescued in BHS. I was desperate to get on but she was obviously keen to talk. She thanked me again for helping her out. She said she could remember how to strip down an engine but didn't seem to be able to manage decimal coinage, even though it's been out for over a year. Apparently, she drove an ambulance during the Great War. By the time I could get away, my lunch hour was up.

Friday 2nd June 1972

I went to see Maria this evening. She lives above her studio, and her front door is just to the left of the studio entrance, with a narrow staircase up to the flat. She let me in without the least sign of embarrassment. It must be strange, talking about private things with someone you've only just met. Rather like suddenly finding you've got a stepsister you never knew you had. I think if that happened to Maria, she would take it in her stride.

She went into the kitchen to make coffee and I was left sitting on a huge sofa in the middle of the room, completely surrounded by pictures of Hugh – on the walls – on the bookcases – on the mantelpiece – everywhere!

Her photos in the flat in Cantilupe Street are all black and white and sort of "arty", but these were full of life and colour. They were nearly all of Hugh – looking very young in some of them with his black curly hair and those startling blue eyes – standing at the top of a mountain in a heroic stance and laughing – paddling a canoe – being buried in the sand by a group of children – holding a glass of wine at a reception with a lot of important looking people – and at his easel, rapt, drawing a Klambi cartoon. I stood up and started to go round the room, looking at them. So many pictures of Hugh! It made me wonder if Hugh had been right about Maria was no longer being in love with him. Maria came in from the kitchen and stood there watching me for a moment with a mug in either hand.

"He's very photogenic," she said, and handed me a mug.

"Yes," I said, and I so wanted to ask her how she felt about him but I couldn't. So I said,

"That letter – the one where he told me about the elephant cave – he said he had told you about us."

"That's right."

"And that you didn't mind?"

"I think you'll be very good for him. I've been waiting for it to happen."

"Oh!" I said, not knowing quite how to react.

"Now, have a look at these!" she said briskly.

She got out some maps and we traced Hugh's journey from Jakarta to the Sacred Cave. It's south of Jakarta – at the foot of Mount Salak. Maria said it was a place where strange things happened – planes crashed – people disappeared – but she thought it was all superstition. I told her what Hugh had said – that his inspiration for "Klambi" had dried up and he needed to go to the cave to find him, and we looked at each other and smiled because it was just so Irish, so Hugh.

It's such a help to see the place on a map. And it's a help to know that Maria is there worrying with me. I think she felt the same about me, which is weird when you think of the circumstances.

Saturday 3rd June 1972

I treated myself to my first strawberries of the year today. Strawberry time last year I didn't know Hugh.

I have reached January 1898 in Flo Chave's diary and she has suddenly mentioned a "Dr Mac". That must be the Dr McCutchan of the photographs and the trunk. She wonders if her letter has offended him. What could she have said in it? It's obviously really important to her that her family likes him. I wonder if it was "Dr Mac" who sent her those flowers. I've got rather fond of Flo. I would so like her to have someone who cares about her and thinks she is special.

I rode my bike out along the Tillington road towards Burghill – pretty shattered by the time I got to the top of the hill. I had my sandwiches there in the churchyard. I closed my eyes and left my hand open on the bench and imagined Hugh's hand in mine. He was very close. I can't believe he's dead. Perhaps some mountain spirit took him and he will reappear years later like that J M Barrie play, thinking he has only been away an hour or so. I will be old and grey and wrinkled and he won't recognise me. If I make it sound like a story, perhaps it will stop being so real and horrible to me.

Sunday 4th June 1972

It's very quiet. I wonder what other single girls do on a Sunday. It's been raining all day and I've got a headache and a sore throat. If I rang my mother, she'd tell me it was all in my mind and I should go for a walk. She would remind me of Shackleton's men on Elephant Island living for months on the odd frozen penguin under an upturned boat.

It's so quiet. Just the clock ticking. And the occasional footsteps going past on the pavement up at ground level. After lunch – tinned spaghetti cooked on top of my Baby Belling – I know how to live – I got out my elephant stuff (how my mind runs on elephants!) and spread it out on the table and just sat there looking at it, thinking, "This is all I shall ever do – make toys for other people's children." And then I threw the pieces all over the room.

"Nasty temper!" I expect Flo would say. But did she ever think like I do – that she would only ever look after other people's children? I bet if she had had a chance for happiness, she wouldn't have thrown it away like I did. I miss Hugh. I miss him turning up unexpectedly on my doorstep. I miss his jokes. Before I met him, I was lonely but I didn't realise I was lonely. Now I know what life can be like and I can't bear to go back to how I was before.

I was telling Jeanie the other day about Hugh's cartoon elephant, Klambi.

"How can you have a comic strip about an elephant nobody can see?" she asked.

"Well, you see people's reactions – and you can see that someone has got squashed by something very large when Klambi sits on their lap."

She couldn't understand how that was funny at all. I suppose you have to see the cartoons.

I have been rooting around in Dr Mac's trunk up in my little attic room, and have discovered that at the time Flo was writing her diary, Mac was Assistant Medical Officer at Burghill Asylum – somewhere near where I was cycling yesterday.

There is a letter giving Dr Mac a reference. It says "he is very courteous, amiable and of kind disposition, and has the confidence of the inmates and Staff, is well up in organising amusements for the patients, and takes part, being musical himself, and has the general interest of the Institution at heart." There are lots of reference letters amongst his things and they all say how kind he is. I feel as if my Flo has fallen into good hands.

Friday 9th June 1972

No news. I ring Maria every day. I keep asking if there is anything I can do. She says there isn't. I think she is probably one of those people who like to keep hold of the reins themselves. But on the other hand, there may really not be anything I can do. That's what's so awful. She said the editor of Hugh's newspaper had been in touch with her asking if he could help. She put him in touch with her contact at the Foreign Office who apparently told him that the situation was "delicate", and publicity about Hugh being missing was not wise at present.

I haven't told Mum and Dad about Hugh. They just wouldn't understand. They'd think "married man – not done!" and that would be that.

I met the decimal coin lady again in the library at lunchtime. Her name is Gwendoline. She mentioned that she lives on the Tillington Rd. I said I had cycled along there the other day. I think she's lonely because she invited me for lunch on Saturday. I couldn't think of an excuse. I'm sure there are going to be lots of those awful silences while we think of something to say. Hell's teeth! as my Hugh would say.

Flo writes in her diary about a girl who was incarcerated by her father for falling in love with a groom. I can't help wondering if Flo was in the same position. Did her parents not want her to be involved with Mac?

Giles asked if we could go cycling together. I said I wanted to go to St Ann's Well in the Malverns. It's where Flo took Mac. Giles might come with me.

The Duke of Windsor has been buried. I wonder what would have happened if he hadn't abdicated. I remember Granny saying what a handsome young man he was.

Saturday 10th June 1972

No word from Maria.

Watched a programme about the *Blue Peter* people burying a time capsule in the grounds of the Television Centre last year. They are going to open it on the first episode of the year 2000. I will be 52. Hugh will be 67. If he makes it.

Sunday 11th June 1972

Still no news. Life goes on. I seem to be two different people. One of me is like a fisherman's wife, facing out to sea, motionless, waiting. The other talks and works and eats as if nothing unusual is happening to her.

My lunch with Gwendoline went better than I expected. She says she likes to be called Gwen. She's 80 but you wouldn't think it. She is very easy to be with. We sat in the garden for a bit and then went indoors for hot quiche and salad and new potatoes. She grows her own vegetables. It was a nice change from fish fingers and frozen peas.

She caught me looking at a photo of a good-looking man in RAF uniform on her piano. She said it was her son. He had been burnt when he crashed his plane and had been in and out of hospitals for years after the War. She said he was very scarred. It must have been awful. Gwen said he would only go out in the village after dark.

Once he was walking in the recreation ground when he suddenly came upon a girl walking her dog. The girl took one look at his face and gasped – obviously terrified. He came home and told Gwen and she said she tried to think of something comforting to say but all she could do was cry, and then it was he who had to comfort her. Gwen said she had never told anyone about that before. I didn't like to ask where he is now in case he's dead.

She asked me if I had a boyfriend, and I said, "Not exactly." And then I told her all about Hugh. I couldn't believe I was talking to a stranger about him. She said she had seen the Klambi cartoons in the paper and they always made her laugh. She seemed excited to think that I knew Hugh and I felt rather proud. She said someone as intelligent as Hugh would be sure to find his way home.

Friday 16th June 1972

Still no news.

Tomorrow Giles and I are cycling to St Ann's Well. Hugh told me once that Elgar learned to ride a bike in 1900 and used to cycle over the Malvern hills with tunes dancing in his head. I wonder if Flo ever passed him on her bike.

Mac and Flo have become engaged! 6th February 1898. They have apparently been going out together for three years. Why didn't she mention him in her diary earlier? They can't have actually spent much time together during those three years because the family were in Australia from 1895 to 1897. Most of the contact between Mac and Flo must have been by letter.

Flo thinks people won't approve and she isn't going to tell anyone outside her family. I wonder why.

Sunday 18ᵗʰ June 1972

Still no news.

I am so stiff today. There are muscles aching where I didn't know I had them. I'm glad I went though. The Malverns are beautiful. We found St Ann's Café, and the building where you can drink the water from St Ann's spring. Giles said that Mac would have cupped his hands for Flo to drink out of so he did that for me. I think in Victorian times they probably would have had a tin cup but I didn't like to disappoint him.

We cycled up a road called Happy Valley. Mac and Flo would have walked along it to get to St Ann's Well. I felt a prickling on the back of my neck when the old café building came into view as if Flo was with me. It was really weird.

We got nearly back to Giles' house in Broomy Hill when his bike got a puncture and we had to wheel our bikes the rest of the way. Alice (with the help of her grandmother) had made a Welcome Home banner and hung it on the gate. If it hadn't been for the puncture, Giles would have insisted on cycling home with me.

Alice's friend, Emily, wants one of my elephants so I must start that tomorrow. Giles calls the elephant I made for Alice, "Trumpet Major".

Monday 19ᵗʰ June 1972

Today is 19ᵗʰ June – the anniversary of the day Hugh and I met. When I think of it, it's like a film running in my head. It was a Saturday. Warm and sunny. I couldn't bear to stay indoors so I broke my weekend rule and went out into the town. Everyone on the streets seemed to have someone with them, and I dashed into the library to escape. There was a poster about an elephant themed exhibition upstairs in the art gallery, so of course I went to have a look. I was standing in front of a picture called *Lost Elephants of Java*. There was a bench next to me and on it was sitting a man in a light-coloured hat. He was drawing something in a sketch pad. I remember thinking that he was awfully large. He was totally engrossed in what he was doing and I was curious to see his drawing, so I casually walked behind the bench to get a better view. The man turned his head suddenly and looked at me under the brim of his hat. Such intense blue eyes!

"Do you want a look? It will be in the paper tomorrow." His voice was deep but soft as if I were a cat or a dog he was trying not to frighten. And that Irish accent!

"Here, won't you sit down, so?" he said, standing up. I remembered everything my mother had told me about not talking to strange men but sat down next to him, anyway. There was something compelling about him. He held the sketch pad so that I could see. The picture was entitled, *Klambi takes a bus ride*. A large woman was lying back in her seat with her arms open as if she were holding something. Her shopping was scattered all over the floor and the other occupants of the bus were all looking at her with various emotions – surprise, sympathy, irritation.

"He's an invisible Javan elephant," Hugh said quietly, and his eyes watched for my reaction. It made me smile. I looked up and he was smiling down at me too, and it was like an electric charge, tingling between us. Tucking the sketch pad under his arm, he took my hand and stood up.

"Come on, let's get the bus!"

"What bus?"

"Any bus."

It was a recognition rather than a meeting. It was as if we had known each other in another lifetime and now we had found each other again. It wouldn't have mattered if the 15 years between us had been 30 years, I would still have loved him.

When he told his sister about us, she talked about it being "an affair". Hugh said it wasn't an affair because affairs are finite. They have a beginning and an end. Ours was a comradeship which would go on for ever, even beyond death.

I feel so happy tonight. Isn't that odd – that I should be happy when I don't know where he is? But when you're in love, you can't help but be happy, and I'm so in love with Hugh.

Tuesday 27th June 1972

Still no news.

Flo has asked her mother to break the news for her to Father about her engagement to Mac. I think I would probably have done the same. She went to an entertainment at Burghill Asylum and says she felt she was acting a part all the evening, and I know exactly what that's like. None of my family know about Hugh.

Giles turned up at my bedsit on Sunday afternoon and asked me to go for a cycle ride. I said I wanted to start on Emily's elephant but he said it was much too nice a day to stay indoors so I hoicked "Klambi" out of the shed and off we went. We ended up having tea at a little café near the river. He asked me laughingly if my boyfriend minded my going out cycling with other men. He's never asked me about my private life before and I think he assumed I didn't have anyone. I told him about Hugh and he went a bit quiet.

Wednesday 28th June 1972

The *Daily Sketch* is re-running some of his old Klambi cartoons. There was a little column saying he was still missing. It looked horribly like an obituary.

Flo says her parents are not elated about her engagement. Is it because they are going to lose the daughter who will care for them in old age? Somehow, they don't strike me as that sort. Must have taken a lot of guts in those days to get engaged to a man your parents disapproved of.

I want to know what happened – why the wheel fell off and they never married. But I'm not going to cheat and look ahead in the diary.

Miss Jancey from the Record Office is coming round from Harold Street tomorrow to look at the glass slides. She's a scary lady, though she's always been nice to me. I expect Giles will be worried about her smoking up in the attic, but I'm not going to be the one to tell her not to!

I thought Mac's trunk was just full of medical textbooks and letters of reference, but there was an envelope tucked down the side with newspaper cuttings in it. They were mostly, I think, about events in the mental asylums where he worked, but one was headed "Presentation to Mr W A McCutchan". He was leaving a little village called Stoke sub Hamdon in Somerset in 1894, and moving to Hereford. They obviously thought a lot of him in the village. The man giving the presentation said he was just as attentive to the poor people as to the rich, which is a nice thought.

If I lose myself in the 1890s, just for a little while I can escape the awful frustration of imagining Hugh in danger and not being able to help him.

Thursday 29th June 1972

No letter from Hugh. Nothing from Maria.

Miss Jancey came to see the glass slides this morning. She brought Stuart Robinson with her who is an expert on Victorian photographs. He wants to develop some of the slides and have an exhibition in the Art Gallery. I like to think that other people will get to see Mac's photos. I asked him if he could let me see them once they are done, and he said yes.

Flo writes in her diary of having time with Mac on her own. After three years of only corresponding by letter, Mac and Flo are only now beginning to get to know each other properly, I think. It must have been difficult for them to be on their own.

Hugh and I were lucky that we had his flat, but I never spent the night there. He had this old-fashioned idea about my reputation. He was born before the War, in Ireland, and into a Catholic family at that. The Swinging Sixties hadn't really reached him. He knew I ached for him just as much as he ached for me, but he wanted us to wait until he was free to marry me. And the fact that we knew we were both prepared to give ourselves to each other was all that mattered, somehow.

I cycled out to see Gwen after work. First of all, I went to have a look at St Mary's Hospital – that's what the Burghill Insane Asylum is called now, and it's just up the road from Gwen's house. I remember there being a mental hospital near to where we lived in Oxford when I was about ten. When people mentioned it, there was a feeling of horror – rather like when people mention Passchendaele or the workhouse or the plague.

St Mary's actually has rather a good feel. The gates were open. I pushed "Klambi" past the lodge and a little way up the drive. It was bigger than I imagined – lots of rather beautifully designed, warm red brick buildings and well-kept gardens. There were some lovely old trees which Mac would have known. People were working in the grounds and there was a peaceful atmosphere.

When I got to Gwen's, I told her I'd been to see the hospital. She said sometimes the patients escaped and there were men in white coats running round the village trying to round them up, but it generally had a good reputation. She said an American aeroplane crashed into the chimney stack there during the War and all the crewmen were killed.

She drew me out into talking about Hugh. She is such a good listener. We sat in her garden and the woodpigeons coo-ed and the moths came out and the air was full of the fragrance of roses. Hugh felt very close.

Gwen said she was worried about me, that she could see the strain in my face. She said as there was nothing I could do except wait, that I should try to find some other interest to take my mind away from it. I told her how I had been sorting out Miss Chave's papers and how I felt I had got close to Flo through her diary. She said that was just the thing – that I should follow my instincts and try to find out more about the people and places Flo talks about. She said she would love to hear more about Flo – would I write to her to let her know what happens in her diary?

I'm so glad I found Gwen. I have this feeling that it was Flo who pushed me into making contact with her that day.

Friday 30ᵗʰ June 1972

No news.

I think I will write to Gwen about Mac and Flo. It will be good to share Flo with someone. No one at the office is particularly interested in her, and she has become real to me. I think Gwen would like it too. She seems lonely, with no family in Hereford. She doesn't drive any more. Someone picks her up and takes her to the WI, but she said it wasn't a very lively branch. She said the last time she went, they had a competition for who could bring along the most attractive door knob. I had this vision of all these women wandering round their houses, deciding which door knob to unscrew. Flo belonged to the Huntington WI. I wonder what that was like.

I was in Johnsons' bookshop at lunchtime. I love that place. It used to be a nonconformist church, and it still has a huge central hall with books on shelves right up to the ceiling, and long, wooden old-fashioned ladders. And then there's the other part – with little staircases and corridors leading into separate tiny rooms. It was in one of those tiny rooms that I came across a leatherbound book called *The Smiling General*. It was published quite recently, in 1969. It's about General Suharto – the Highest Authority of the Republic of Indonesia. I bought it. I want to know as much as I can about the place where Hugh has disappeared. It's called the "authorised version".

Giles has asked me if I would be his partner at the Mayor's Charity Ball at the Shire Hall. I can't think why. He must know lots of girls who are more suitable. I was going to say no but yesterday I came across an invitation among Flo's stuff from "The Mayor of Hereford and Mrs Chave" – to a Fancy Dress Ball at the Shire Hall in 1892

– "Dancing at 9 o'clock prompt." So, I said yes. That Flo has a lot to answer for.

Now I'm wondering what on earth to wear. There's my Laura Ashley dress but I don't think that will look quite right for a ball. Suppose I have to dance? I don't know how to do that old-fashioned stuff. What have I let myself in for?

The Basement Flat
Albert House
Portland Street
Hereford

Saturday 1st July 1972

Dear Gwen

You wanted to know about Flo Chave and her diary. I hope you don't regret this! I have nobody else to share Flo with. Well, you can always use my letters as firelighters if it all gets too much. You said if I DID decide to write to you, that I shouldn't mention Hugh in my letters because this is supposed to be taking my mind off things. So that is the very last time I will mention him in my letters until I write and tell you that he has come home.

Flo's diary starts in 1897 when she is 30 years old. I don't know when it ends because I am not allowing myself to look any further ahead than the next page. Flo lives with her parents and her sister, Mabel, and her brother, Tom. She also has two more brothers called Hewitt and Harold, and a sister in Australia called Ivy. The living arrangements seem quite fluid – not only do Flo and her parents move backwards and forwards from Devon to Malvern to Hereford, but the people staying in the household change as well. Obviously, Flo didn't write her diary for me but for herself and she knew who all these people were and where she was situated when she wrote it, so sometimes you have to be a bit of a Sherlock to work it all out.

She seems a very go-ahead sort of a girl. She and her cousin, Carrie Langdon, cycled all the way from Torquay to Bristol and then back to a little village called Cove in Devon. No chaperones or anything. The day after they got back to Cove, she said what a shame it was that it was raining and she couldn't go out! Most people would want to put their feet up after a journey like that on a bike!

I think Flo is fond of animals. She mentions them a lot in her diary. She has an Australian white cockatoo called Billie who is always getting into trouble, and there always seems to be a dog around.

She describes places she has been and books she has read. It has been fun following her trail. I have never spent so much time in the library before. I don't know what I would have done without her these last few months. But I am not going to talk about that.

The first entry is July 1897, but Mac doesn't appear until January 1898. I got very excited when I reached the entry for 6th February 1898 because that was when Flo and Mac became engaged. "We agreed God willing our lives should some day be one though our prospects at present are hopeless." Flo doesn't go in for commas. Flo says their relationship has been going on for three years. The family all went out to Australia in the spring of 1895 for the wedding of Flo's sister, Ivy, and they didn't come back until the spring of 1897 so for most of their three-year relationship, they would have had to communicate by letter. How I wish I had those letters!

I hope the WI was a bit more exciting this month.

Love

Jane

PS You WILL let me talk about You Know Who when we meet, though, won't you?

The Basement Flat
Albert House
Portland Street
Hereford

Sunday 2nd July 1972

Dear Gwen

Mac has brought Flo some rings to choose her engagement ring from. She has chosen a plain one ("I dislike the look of stones in the morning") in the form of a true lover's knot. She tells Mac he must give her a dress ring when he is wealthy. She is starting to know him well enough to tease him. They are late for tea on purpose so as to have more time to themselves. Earlier on in the diary she wrote that he was more in love with her than she with him. I think perhaps now it's more balanced.

Her brother, Tom, has been unkind about Mac. When Mac came to visit, Tom was nice to his face but afterwards said to Flo that he was "dead alive" and he didn't think much of him. Poor Flo was awfully upset. She says bitterly that her sister, Ivy, was wise, getting married out in Australia where "the opinion of her relatives cannot wound her... and that of strangers doesn't matter." I wonder if brother Tom misses Ivy and is upset at the thought of another sister getting married and leaving home. Everyone must have thought that Flo was going to stay at home always and then this chap, Mac, comes along and threatens to take her away. Flo's emotions must be seesawing – the excitement and joy of being with Mac, and then the hurt at her family's reactions. I do feel for her.

Dragging you back to 1972 – Giles has invited me to the Mayor's Charity Ball at the Shire Hall! You will be pleased that I am getting out and doing things, but I have an uneasy feeling he thinks I can do those old-fashioned dances. I can't.

Much love

Jane

Tuesday 4th July 1972

Dear Gwen

Something terrible has happened! You remember Flo's younger brother, Harold, who was coming home from Australia? He has died on the ship on the way home. Flo has the awful job of telling her parents. "It was the hardest task I have ever had to do in my life." Mac has rushed round to see her after work, having heard the news in the morning.

They are such a close family. The poor parents! Harold was only 18. Flo was 12 when he was born so she must have been a little mother to him. Things will never be the same for any of them again.

Love

Jane

JANE'S DIARY

Tuesday 4th July 1972

No news.

Flo's younger brother, Harold, has died aged 18. Flo was 12 years older. Things will never be the same for the Chave family again. If Hugh dies, nothing will be the same for me again. I think I would want to become a nun like those kind nuns in Malta when I was boarding at the convent school. I suppose I should have to become a Catholic first.

Rob has offered to lend me the money for a new dress for the ball. He and Mum and Dad are all pleased, I think, that I am getting out at last! I am going shopping on Saturday for what Gwen would call a "frock".

I shall pretend I am going with Hugh. I wonder what colour he would like me to get.

Wednesday 5th July 1972

No news.

Hugh once told me about a painting called *The Fall of Icarus*, where the tragedy is happening in one part of the picture but life goes on around just the same. It's a bit like that with the death of Flo's brother. One minute she's talking about what happened to him and then she's off to Cox and Painter's to get a cycling outfit.

Stuart Robinson rang the office this afternoon. He says would I like to come and look at the prints he has had developed from Mac's glass plate negatives. Oooh! Can't wait for tomorrow.

It is a lovely evening. I can't actually see the sunset through the bars of my basement window but I know it is beautiful from the light. I have been swanning about in my new dress. I do wish Hugh could see me because I think I look rather nice. The dress is a silvery, lilac/green, figure-hugging sort of a thing which clings to my tummy and bum but then flares gracefully out to my feet. It's the loveliest dress I've ever had.

I've been remembering dancing to Diana Ross with Hugh one night here in my bedsit, and I'm sitting here imagining his arms around me and the music playing.

The ball is on the 15th. I am thinking of having my hair cut into a bob. It seems heartless to be thinking about my appearance when who knows what is happening to Hugh.

The Basement Flat
Albert House
Portland Street
Hereford

Thursday 6th July 1972

Dear Gwen

You know those photos of Mac's which the Record Office
were having printed off? Guess what? There is one of Mac!
He's not how we imagined him but he does look rather nice.

He actually looks sort of foreign and I thought – how
can that be, with a name like McCutchan? But then when
I got back to the office, I rooted around in the bundle of
references to see if I could find any mention of where he
came from and found a letter he had written to the Medical
Department of Edinburgh University. He wrote that his
brother in INDIA had paid for him to come to Edinburgh
to study medicine but that this brother had died and he
was having to take work as a Medical Assistant to pay
for his medical studies. So, was he part Indian, perhaps?
Was that why Flo and her family thought people wouldn't
approve of her engagement?

ALSO... Among the photos are some which Mac took
of Flo and her family at the Moor House!!! There are
some sweet ones of Flo sitting in downstairs window,
smiling as she looks down at a cat on her lap. Mr Chave
sits in a wicker chair outside. You can see why Flo was so
attached to him. He has lively, twinkling eyes. You know
in Victorian photos, people generally don't smile or have
any expressions on their faces? Well, Mac's aren't like

that. The people are smiling – specially the children – just as if Mac has been telling them a joke. You get the feeling from the photos that the people having their pictures taken liked him.

Flo's youngest sister, Ivy, is very pretty – obviously the beauty of the family and the only sister to get married. Mac must have taken the photo of her before she left for Australia in 1895.

Mabel – the sister closest in age to Flo – looks stern. She had a university degree and taught in a school.

People are being very nice to Flo's family after Harold's death. Mac was not looking well but "did not complain". I suppose you wouldn't complain about your own problems when your loved one was in such trouble. Dear old Mac! – I'm beginning to sound like Flo!

Flo is consoling herself with her "work" – an afternoon tea cloth and some carving. It is what I do when I am sad. Sorry – shouldn't have said that. Love Jane

JANE'S DIARY

Thursday 6th July 1972

Nothing from Hugh.

Wrote a long letter to Gwen about Mac's photos. Knowing what Mac and Flo looked like around the time they met brings them very close. As I wrote to Gwen, my mind was full of how they felt about each other. I put the letter into an envelope and sealed it and immediately my worry for Hugh flooded back again.

I got out Hugh's letters and reread them. I made myself so sad that it drove me to my battered old suitcase to find the fabric for the elephant I am going to make for Alice's friend, Emily. The case belonged to my grandmother. There's a divider in it. One side is full of jumbled pieces of fabric and the other is quite tidy, really, with tins of buttons and pins and an old cardboard box full of reels of silk and cotton threads. When I open a button tin or a box, I see my grandmother's hands, slender and blue veined, with arthritic knuckles. I used to stay with her in the school holidays sometimes when my parents were abroad. She taught me to sew. Her house was an oasis in the awfulness of my school days. When she had her stroke, we moved in with her on Aylestone Hill. Now that she has died, it still seems to me to be more her house than my parents'.

I started out using Simplicity patterns but for ages now I have been designing my own. This one is going to be a very cuddly elephant – almost as I imagine Klambi would look if he weren't invisible. I found just the right material. I ironed it, pinned the pattern on and cut out the shapes, and just for a few minutes I found myself humming and happy again.

Friday 7th July 1972

Gwen and I met for coffee in town today. We were talking about how poor Mac has got 'flu and Flo is very worried. I remember when Hugh had bronchitis last winter. Maria was staying in the Cantilupe flat and looking after him. I couldn't contact him. I thought that was the worst time of my life. I didn't know what was coming.

I told Gwen that Flo has had a birthday and listed her birthday presents but she doesn't mention one from Mac. Gwen said she couldn't imagine he wouldn't have given her something, but perhaps he couldn't get it because he was ill. Or perhaps it was something so special that she didn't want to talk about it, even in her diary. I think Flo is becoming as real to Gwen as she is to me.

Gwen says she will teach me the waltz so that I can impress Giles at the Ball. I remember having dance lessons at that school in Malta – the one I was in for six months while Dad was stationed there. Mum and Dad took me away because they were afraid I was turning Catholic. "Religion is all very well in its place," Dad said. I remember wondering if God knew where that place was. Anyway, I didn't get to learn the waltz. I got put out of the room for fooling around. I wasn't actually fooling around – I just fell over my partner's feet rather a lot. After that, I went to that awful boarding school in Oxford. I liked the school in Malta. The nuns were kind. Dad says, "now that that chap, Mintoff, is in, there's always trouble." I don't know anything about politics.

It has been so hot today. I opened the tiny window in my attic at work but it didn't make much difference. These warm nights, I want Hugh even more. I lie on top of my bed and remember. His hands, so gentle. I wonder if Flo wanted her lover as much as I want Hugh.

Saturday 8th July 1972

Dear Gwen

You will be relieved to hear that Mac is alright. Phew! I was worried that the 'flu might have carried him off and that was the reason they never got married. All is well. He is convalescing rapidly. Flo wasn't able to say goodbye to him before the family moved again – leaving the hotel in Malvern and moving to a house in Hele in Devon. It is April 1898. The family spend a lot of time in Devon. Both of Flo's parents come from Devon farming families. You can see that in Flo. She is a very sensible, practical sort of a girl!

Flo packed her Saratoga. Have you ever heard of a Saratoga? I hadn't. I looked it up. It's like a pirate's treasure trunk. Flo has lots of hobbies – chip carving and drawn thread work etc. I suppose she needs a big trunk to carry it all down to Devon.

The family like their new house. It seems Mr Chave bought it without the rest of the family seeing it! They have a gardener called Garrish who aired all the blankets and the rooms before they arrived. An odd task for a gardener. They are obviously fed up with living in a hotel and glad to be in their own place. Flo and Mac will have to resort to writing letters to each other again.

Thank you so much for offering to teach me to waltz.
Prepare to be patient! I'll see you on Monday, about 7.30.

Love

Jane

JANE'S DIARY

Saturday 8th July 1972

I went into Johnsons' bookshop today. In the poetry
section was a little book by Laurence Hope – I had a flick
through and noticed the poems were written by someone
who lived in India. Anything to do with India or Java
pulls me in immediately nowadays. I had to buy it. I spent
the evening reading it. There is one poem called "Fate has
no tears." Terrifically sentimental but it has got to me.

"Just as my life once more was waking,
As roses waken late in May,
Fate, blindly cruel and havoc-making,
Stepped in and carried you away."

It was me and Hugh. And then –

"Ah! well-beloved, I never told you,
I did not show in speech or song,
How at the end I longed to fold you,
Close in my arms; so fierce and strong
The longing grew to have and hold you,
You, and you only, all life long."

Sunday 9th July 1972

I have been reading my *Smiling General* book about General Suharto. He started out life as a peasant and worked his way up. All through his childhood, he was passed from one person to another – all supposedly to give him a good future but I don't think it can have been very helpful for building attachments to people. He sounds very sensible and full of integrity but I have an uneasy feeling that I am not getting the whole truth. I had no idea that Indonesia used to be owned by the Dutch. I wish I weren't so ignorant. I could use the excuse of moving schools so often but I think it is more likely that I just dreamed my way through school.

The book is making me feel uneasy. There are so many different factions over there and the army is so powerful.

The Basement Flat
Albert House
Portland Street
Hereford

Tuesday 11th July 1972

Dear Gwen

Thank you so much for my waltz lesson. It was really good fun and I'm so glad I didn't break any of your ornaments! Giles is going to be impressed. I feel ever so much more confident about the ball now.

Poor Mac must have been really ill with the 'flu. Flo says he "had found writing even too great an effort." Poor chap!

The family desperately need another servant down in Devon, but all the local girls work at the paper mill. Fortunately, while on a walk to Bradninch, the family meet a policeman who suggests a possible maid and points them in the right direction. Can you imagine that happening nowadays? "Excuse me, officer, could you tell me where I could find a good girl?"

Love

Jane

JANE'S DIARY

Wednesday 12th July 1972

Maria came round to see me this evening. She hadn't been to my flat before. I was horribly aware of the fact I hadn't swept the carpet for ages and there was washing up in the sink and clothes all over the place, but after she had told me I ought to get my front doorbell mended, and asked if I had decaffeinated coffee (did I have what?) I felt more at ease somehow. I think if she had been polite, I would have been more uncomfortable.

I asked her to tell me what she knew about Java. She was very scathing about my book on General Suharto. He is not the ideal leader described in my *Smiling General* book. In fact, he engineered a horrific massacre of the Communists by the army in 1965. Maria said the massacres are no longer going on – but the situation is still pretty unstable and you can be arrested at the drop of a hat if you have the slightest connection with the Communist party.

What was Hugh thinking of, going out there? I know. Elephants. My darling, idiotic Hugh.

I asked Maria if there was anything I could do. She said she is keeping up the pressure on the Foreign Office who in turn are on to the Indonesian authorities but apart from that, we can't do anything. They know now where he was heading for but they don't know if he got into trouble before he got there, or on the way back or what, and it's a huge area. And how do we know that the authorities are actually bothering to do anything at all?

As she was getting up to leave, Maria noticed my collection of elephants on top of the bookcase. She asked me to take them down for her to see them up close. There was my first little elephant, Chloe, and then after that loads more, as well as the special ones. "Harriet" – I made after my grandmother died. "Maurice" came about when I decided to leave school half way through my 'A' levels. And then, of course, there's "Hugh". I don't always make elephants because I am sad – sometimes it is when I feel so bouncy and full of joy that I have to pour it into something.

I remember Hugh wanted me to give him his elephant but I wouldn't. I wanted to keep it in case anything happened to the real Hugh. I must have had a premonition. It was the only thing I ever said "no" to Hugh about – except when he asked me to go to Java and get married.

Thursday 13th July 1972

Gwen wrote to wish me luck at the ball and to ask me over to dinner next Thursday. Her granddaughter, Jennifer, is coming to stay with her. Jennifer is the daughter of the man in the photograph – the one whose face was scarred by burns. I thought he might have died but apparently he didn't. He was looked after in hospital after the war by Archibald McIndoe – the doctor who used to give his patients pale ale. The patients at his hospital started a club called the Guinea Pig Club, and Geoffrey (Gwen's son) used to go to their meetings in London after the war. It was when he was up at one of these get togethers that he met the sister of another ex-patient and he married her.

So, Geoffrey is alive and kicking and living in Worcester. And his daughter, Jennifer, is coming to stay with Gwen next week. I wonder what she's like.

The Basement Flat
Albert House
Portland Street
Hereford

Thursday 13th July 1972

Dear Gwen

Flo's brother, Hewitt, seems to be in favour of Flo's engagement. Flo writes in her diary that Hewitt met Mac in Hereford, and Mac told him he was planning to come to Torquay to see Flo. Now, did Hewitt search out Mac on Flo's behalf, or did he just meet him by chance? I like to think of Hewitt as Flo's go-between.

Mac arrives in Torquay and stays with Flo's aunts Sophie and Elise. "The ordeal went off very well," Flo writes, and then mentions they went off to the dining room to have a smoke and a chat. Surely Flo didn't smoke? The aunts obviously don't think they have to chaperone them every minute. Aunt Sophie is unmarried, while Aunt Elise was widowed young. I'm not sure whether Sophie has a bike, but I know Elise went cycling with Flo when she was living in Devon last year. Sometimes, Gwen, I'm not quite sure which century I'm living in.

Love

Jane

PS Thank you for your good luck card. By the time I see you this time next week, the ball will be over. Looking forward to meeting Jennifer.

JANE'S DIARY

Sunday 16ᵗʰ July 1972

Well, the ball has happened, and that's not all.

Giles and I arrived at the Shire Hall with loads of other taxis. There were women getting out of them wearing long dresses and high heels and masses of jewellery, and the men all in bow ties. Passing our statue – the George Cornewall Lewis one which Hugh lifted me up onto – I felt as if I was waving goodbye to my last friend before stepping off the plank. I gripped Giles' hand tightly as we climbed the steps and he smiled at me and squeezed mine back. We went up those imposing stairs and paused at the door to the hall. They actually announce you, like in the films.

After that it was less formal. People were milling about talking loudly and an orchestra was playing "Moon River". There was free wine. Well, I suppose Giles had paid a huge amount of dosh for the tickets so it wasn't really free. I tried hard not to drink mine too quickly in case it went to my head and I made a fool of myself but I was so nervous that sipping gave me something to do and I was soon through my first glass. I wasn't the only nervous one. Lots of people were looking ill at ease to start with. You could see them suddenly recognising a couple they knew and making a beeline for them. Giles caught sight of a man he knew and grabbed me by the elbow.

"There's John Constance! Come on!"

After that it was easier, except that John's wife is my doctor and I kept hoping she wasn't remembering that the last time she saw me she was doing an internal. When I told them I was Giles' secretary, they weren't quite sure what to say. I had several offers of dancing, though. I felt like Flo and wanted to say, "I'm sorry but my dance card is quite full up." Actually, I just smiled and said "No, thank you," or "Sorry, I'm not dancing." Six courses at the dinner! It was set on long tables in a square with one side missing. All the dignitaries sat at the middle one. I was sitting next to an elderly chap with a little beard who is writing a history of Hereford so I pumped him for news of 1898. He asked why I was so interested and I told him all about Mac and Flo. Giles, sitting opposite me, was nabbed by a very talkative lady on his right but I could see him glancing across every time she drew breath, to make sure I was alright.

After dinner, they had a charity auction. Golly, there's some money about! Giles didn't buy anything – said it was out of his league.

And then, when the auction was over, the orchestra played some more modern stuff and Giles pulled me up on the dance floor. You have never seen anything so funny as Giles trying to dance! It would have been embarrassing if I hadn't had three glasses of wine and one of Tia Maria. He gave up after that one attempt and we went round the tables talking to people Giles knew.

Then the orchestra started playing, "Can't Help Falling in Love With You". Giles looked at me and raised his eyebrows and I found myself on the dance floor – waltzing! I was actually enjoying it – I even managed to look at Giles instead of my feet after a bit.

It was then that it happened. The music stopped and Giles kissed me on the lips. Perhaps he had drunk more than I realised. I don't know. I only know it didn't feel right. I would have liked to have gone home right then, but I couldn't embarrass him by leaving him on the dance floor on his own. He took my arm and guided me back to my seat. As I sat down, he leaned over me and said, "You didn't mind, did you?" – but not as if he expected me to say yes. So of course, I said no. What else can you say?

He's been good to me – giving me the bike and going to St Ann's with me and inviting me to the ball, but I only want him as a friend. Perhaps it didn't mean anything, that kiss.

Sunday 16th July 1972

Dear Gwen

There is a comfortable feeling about Flo's growing relationship with Mac. She says he is an interesting companion and "So fond of the birds." You feel she is thinking, "Yes, I've done the right thing getting engaged to this man I really don't know that well." She and Mac have spent Sunday and Monday at Aunt Sophie's in Torquay, and have taken the train to Hele, where the Chaves are living, on the Tuesday afternoon. The trains must have made a huge difference to people's lives. They zip around everywhere on them.

Love

Jane

PS Will tell you all about the ball on Thursday. My waltzing was magnifique!

PPS Can I bring anything?

The Basement Flat
Albert House
Portland Street
Hereford

Monday 17th July 1972

Dear Gwen

You will never believe what has happened. If you read it in a book, you would think it was much too far-fetched to be real! You remember the maid the family found in Bradninch via the policeman? They called her Mary but her real name was Ellen. Wasn't it weird how people changed their servants' names in those days? Perhaps it was so that they could remember them more easily or something. I should hate to be called something different, even though Jane is not exactly exotic.

Anyway, to go back to Flo's diary – Mary (or Ellen) tells Flo's mother that she recognises Mac. She met him when he used to work for Dr Walter in Stoke sub Hamdon. Of all the villages in Devon, they find a maid living there who worked in Stoke sub Hamdon in Somerset! She says such nice things about him – how he was "greatly beloved" and "so good to the poor". I suppose Mac knew what it was like to be poor, having to work to pay for his medical studies. Mary/Ellen mentions "his testimonial", which I suppose was the send-off which the Stoke people gave him when he left the village. Mary/Ellen shows Flo's mother some photographs he gave her which she has treasured. "If Miss Florrie is engaged to him, she will have a good husband," she says.

You can imagine that Flo is over the moon about it. At last, her family have an independent opinion – and a good one – of Mac's character!

He has given her the engagement ring which she likes very much. She had another ring which was too big, so he gives her a little one to keep that one on. What a thoughtful chap he is! Flo now has no doubts about him – he just needs "fortune to favour him in the way of a berth" – a good job, I suppose, and enough money to marry her. I wish in a way the diary could stop here in a happy bit because I know Flo never gets married.

Love

Jane

JANE'S DIARY

Friday 21st July 1972

No news about Hugh.

I met Gwen's granddaughter last night – Jenny. She is a nurse at Hatton Hospital in Warwickshire – what used to be the Hatton Lunatic Asylum. It's weird how my life seems to be full of asylums at the moment! Hatton sounds pretty grim, from what she was telling us.

Jenny is a few years older than me, with Gwen's sense of humour and original way of looking at things. You can't imagine either of them feeling sorry for themselves, but that doesn't stop them being sympathetic towards other people. She's taller than me, which isn't difficult. She's pretty. Her hair's the colour of homemade custard and she wears it in a pony tail. She's got a lovely relationship with Gwen. She doesn't patronise her for being old. It must be refreshing for Gwen to be treated as a person rather than an OAP.

Friday 21st July 1972

Dear Gwen

Thank you so much for the meal last night. It was lovely, and it was nice to meet Jenny. Isn't she easy to talk to? I feel as if I've known her for ages. I'm sorry she isn't very happy where she works. I do hope she can get another job nearer Hereford so that you can see her more often.

Flo and her mother went to a funeral service at the local church. Flo says she will never like the hymn "Thy will be done" again – too many sad memories of Harold's death. I remember my mother saying that about "The Lord is my Shepherd" – because it reminded her of my grandmother's funeral. Flo's sister, Ivy, has written from Australia about Harold, having just heard about his death, and now Flo is dreaming about him.

On a lighter note, the family seem to have taken on a hideous dog called "Tiger" with the house, and have been giving him a wash. Miss Lloyd has arrived from Hereford on a visit, and Hewitt has cycled all the way from Exeter "in a dreadful laver".

Lots of love

Jane

JANE'S DIARY

Sunday 23rd July 1972

No news.

I went to Mass this morning at that big Catholic church in Broad Street – the one with the pillars. Since writing in my diary about Malta and the convent, I've felt I wanted to go to church. It is a very imposing building and I was nervous about going in. I went to the 8 o'clock. There weren't many people there. I lit a candle for Hugh after Mass. The little flame looked all blurry through my tears, but they were happy tears in a way because he felt so close. Outside on the steps, two of the little old ladies came up to me to chat. They said they wished I could have seen the church in the old days. The building has become a bit dilapidated since then. They said the 10 a.m. Mass was much livelier, with guitars and singing. I think they thought, being young, I would enjoy that better, but actually I liked the quiet service very much.

Came home and began work on "Emily". As I started threading my needle rhythmically in and out, making tiny stitches, I seemed to hear the sound of Hugh's pencil moving over paper, then the sound of Elgar's Variation XIII – Hugh's favourite. I wasn't sitting in my bedsit. I was curled up in my favourite armchair in his studio in Cantilupe Street, sewing a tail onto an elephant while Hugh worked on a Klambi cartoon, his pipe at the corner of his mouth. He always had music playing while he painted or drew cartoons. It could be Irish folk music, or the Stones, or Bach, but when he drew Klambi it was inevitably Elgar. Sometimes, I would be concentrating, head down, on my elephant sewing, and I would hear that laugh of his, a sort of a quiet, hiccoughy laugh, and

I would put my sewing down and go over to see what he had drawn. He would look at me with one eyebrow up as if to say, "Well? Is it funny?" And it always was.

Monday 24th July 1972

Dear Gwen

Flo and her family have taken up croquet. Father and Hewitt have bought a set.

Tom has been given an umbrella for his birthday. For a wealthy family, they don't go to town on birthday presents. But perhaps in 1898 an umbrella was a luxury item.

Mac has come to stay again and Father has taken him out for a drive. I wonder what they talked about. He is getting better after his 'flu, and is taking photographs.

That is the Chave bulletin for today.

Love

Jane

JANE'S DIARY

Tuesday 25th July 1972

No news.

Gwen's granddaughter, Jenny, turned up at work today. I was in with Giles, handing him a letter to sign, and she walked straight past Jeanie's desk and into Giles' office.

"Hi, Jane! Got an hour or two to spare for lunch?"

Giles rocketed to his feet as if she were the Queen and I could see this struck Jenny as funny. I've never seen him quite so taken off his guard before. He seemed quite impressed with my having such a dynamic friend. I said I had to be back at one and Giles said, "No, no – take your time!"

So, we did. Jenny had made up a picnic and brought a bottle of cider and we sat by the river under one of those weeping willows. She told me about her love life – she has had an on/off relationship with a man called Eddie which seems to be finally off now – and I told her about Hugh. I wondered if her grandmother might have told her something about my situation but I don't think she had. That's what I love about Gwen. You can tell her anything and you know it won't go any further.

I didn't get back to work till gone half past one! Jenny said she would come in with me to make sure I didn't get told off but I said not to worry – Giles and I were friends as well as boss and secretary and it would be alright. She said, "He's rather a dish, isn't he?" I never thought of him that way before. My mind always turns to ostriches when I think of Giles. Hugh once started doodling an ostrich, and for some reason the head turned out to be Giles's, with deep-set eyes and an aristocratic beak.

Wednesday 26th July 1972

Dear Gwen

Mac and Flo have been shown round Bradninch Church. Flo said the screen is very curious. So, I looked it up in the library and there was a picture of the naked Eve on it. I wonder if that is why Flo said it was curious. Do you suppose she was a bit embarrassed looking at a naked woman with Mac beside her?

Did Jenny tell you about our picnic? I hope you have had a good weekend with her. Give her my love when you speak to her next.

Jane

JANE'S DIARY

Thursday 27th July 1972

My doorbell gave a squirk this evening. It was Maria. She said quickly before I could get my hopes up (but it was too late) that she didn't have any news.

She had come round about my elephants. She said the owner of the gift shop next to her studio is interested in selling my elephants and would I take a couple in to show her? I couldn't quite believe it.

If it were someone other than Maria suggesting it, I would probably say no but nobody says no to Maria. The shop is in the centre of Hereford and sells really upmarket stuff. I don't mind some of them going, but "Hugh" is definitely staying here with me.

After Maria had gone, I was rooting about in my wardrobe for more elephants, when little "Chloe" fell off the top of the wardrobe onto my head. She was my first ever elephant. I made her when I was staying with my grandmother for the Easter holidays – I was ten. I remember that because I read somewhere that ten was the happiest age to be and I remember thinking, oh no it wasn't. I was at a particularly beastly school at the time where nobody spoke to me except one girl, Elizabeth. She was kind to me. And then she left the school.

My grandmother heard me crying in the night, and came into my bedroom to find out what was wrong. Granny said to cheer up because she had a surprise for me, and the next day she showed me a pattern for a little elephant and we started working together on "Chloe". She was rather wonky in the bottom department and her ears weren't quite right but she was my very first elephant and I loved her. I think I must always have had a thing about elephants. Granny said when I was little, I used to call them "elefumps".

Friday 28th July 1972

No news. Is this how it will be? Just no news no news over and over again? Eventually, Hugh will be "presumed dead" and nobody will ever know what has happened to him. I daren't let that possibility into my mind for more than a second.

Giles was asking me about the Chave records today. I told him about Mac and Flo and how they had got engaged, but her family weren't enthusiastic about it. I told him about the glass negatives and how Mac had worked at Stoke sub Hamdon, and how he had been liked by the villagers because he cared for the poor just as well as he cared for the wealthy. I said I would like to cycle to Stoke sub Hamdon one day, following in Flo's footsteps.

Giles said, why didn't we do it together? He said he couldn't spare the time to cycle the whole way, but we could put our bikes on the train to Yeovil and then cycle the rest of the way. Being put on the spot like that, I couldn't think of an excuse to say no, so I think we seem to be doing it.

The Basement Flat
Albert House
Portland Street
Hereford

Tuesday 1st August 1972

Dear Gwen

Etta Baker has been to stay with Flo in Devon. She lives in Hereford and is the stepdaughter of a Dr Henry Moore who was born at Lucknow. It's interesting that both he and Dr Morrison (Mac's boss at Burghill) were born in India like Mac. I suppose because of the Empire there was a lot of to-ing and fro-ing between India and Britain.

Have you heard of Egremont Folly? Mac and Flo have been to visit it.

Giles and I are going to cycle to Stoke sub Hamdon where Mac used to work. I'm a bit worried about doing it with Giles after what I told you happened at the ball, but at the same time really excited to be seeing where Mac lived.

Love

Jane

JANE'S DIARY

Thursday 3rd August 1972

No news.

To begin with, I was ringing Maria every day, but then I thought it was making her miserable to have to keep saying "no news" so I stopped. I knew she would tell me the minute she heard anything. But then after a few days I started doubting that and panicked and rang her again. And that's been the pattern for weeks now.

Last night I went round to Broomy Hill to make plans with Giles for our expedition. Giles has lived with his mother since his wife died. Their house is one of those sturdy, 1930s buildings, with a big garden front and back. As I stood at the front door with its interesting coloured glass above the lintel, I thought it was the sort of house I wouldn't mind living in, but once inside, I felt differently. There is a coldness to it. The furniture is all a bit formal looking. I should imagine it hasn't changed since Giles' parents moved in after they were married.

Little Alice let me in.

"Good evening!" she said.

I do love that child! She said she had something to show me and led the way to her bedroom.

"It's the Major," said Alice, putting her elephant carefully onto my lap. "Spook got hold of him and he's hurt." Spook is their marmalade cat. He's one of those cats which you can stroke twice but the third time you'd better look out.

After I'd sorted the Major out with the help of her grandmother's sewing basket, Alice went to bed and Giles and I looked at railway timetables and maps of the area round Yeovil. We're going on 17th August, staying the night in a local pub and coming back the next day. Vanessa seemed very interested in it all. I wonder if perhaps she thinks Giles and I are an item and how she feels about that. I shouldn't imagine her wanting anyone muscling in and taking over her granddaughter. Although my mind is full of Hugh, I can't help being excited at the thought of seeing Montacute and Ham Hill, and the little village with its honey-coloured stone cottages. I want to see the house where Mac lived.

The Basement Flat
Albert House
Portland Street
Hereford

Saturday 5th August 1972

Dear Gwen

I have been doing some digging and have discovered that when Mac is described as Anglo-Indian, it doesn't mean that he was half English and half Indian, as we thought. It turns out he is French on his mother's side and Scottish on his father's side. From Mr & Mrs Chave's point of view, though, he was still foreign and broke and working in a mental asylum!

Mac is still staying in Hele with Flo in the diary at present. He went missing on his bike and didn't get back till 11 p.m. Flo writes very calmly in her diary, "I was thankful to see him arrive," but she gives herself away by saying that her aunts kindly stayed up with her till he was safely back, so she was obviously horribly worried about him. The next day is Sunday. "Mac and I spent a very quiet but happy day."

Giles and I have been planning our trip to Stoke sub Hamdon. He doesn't seem to be reading anything into it. No question of sharing a room at the pub!

Love

Jane

JANE'S DIARY

Monday 7ᵗʰ August 1972

When I went into work this morning, Giles came out of his office with the *Times* in his hand.

"Did you see this in the paper? Is this where your chap, Hugh, is?"

It was about a big operation against the Communists in Western Sarawak. It said more than 1,500 Malaysian troops and police were engaged in a big operation against Communist guerrillas in western Sarawak. They had been rounding up suspected Communists and there was a 24-hour curfew. I showed him where it was on the map of Indonesia I keep on the wall behind my desk. It's a completely different island to Java. It still made my tummy lurch, though, knowing that such things are going on out there.

And I am nearly, very nearly at the end of Flo's diary. When I started reading it, it was going to be a magic charm – Hugh would be back when I reached the end. If I finish Flo's diary and there is still no news of Hugh, I will have nothing to cling on to. Or if Flo's diary ends with the reason why she doesn't marry Mac and it's tragic – will that be a sign that Hugh is not coming back?

I am almost too scared to go on reading.

Tuesday 8th August 1972

Dear Gwen

I have come to the end of the diary. And it doesn't tell me ANYTHING about what happened to the two of them! Mac leaves for London, and Flo says she is sorry he has to go but the best of friends must part. It is SUCH an anti-climax!

I feel quite lost.

Yours, bereft

Jane

JANE'S DIARY

Tuesday 8ᵗʰ August 1972

Reached the last page of Flo's diary today. 20ᵗʰ July 1898. No hint of why they never married. I feel as if Flo has vanished from my life as utterly as Hugh.

I had just written that and was just about to go to bed, when the doorbell did its thing. It was Maria. Said could she come in and talk for a minute? I could see she was agitated and my heart was bumping like anything as I let her in.

She had seen a report in the paper that Amnesty International have asked President Suharto to release untried political prisoners. They say there are at least 70,000 of these – people who "have been members or sympathizers of the Communist Party" who were involved with the coup of 1965.

Maria wonders if perhaps Hugh might have got arrested because they thought he was a Communist, and that's why we haven't heard anything from him. She is going to try to find out. I don't know whether to be relieved there is a possibility he is alive, or worried that he is in some horrible prison being mistreated. My mind is full of the most awful pictures.

But it's weird that Maria should have this idea today, just as I have finished Flo's diary. It's as if Flo is trying to tell me something. And at least the news is not the worst.

PART 2 – PRISON

JANE'S DIARY

Wednesday 9th August 1972

I went round to Maria's after work. She said she had spoken to her man in the Foreign Office today and he is going to "make enquiries."

I went to the library at lunchtime and asked them if they had anything about prisons in Indonesia. The librarian found a report by Amnesty International. It begins:

"Indonesia presents a problem which is almost unique in its size and complexity."

Well, that was a good start.

Apparently, martial law was set up in 1957, with Army officers taking over government positions, and the only challenge to the growing power of the army was the PKI – the Indonesian Communist Party. The attempted coup by the PKI in 1965, which Maria told me about, was followed by half a million people being killed and more than three quarters of a million people being arrested.

The report said that the sole proof of complicity in the coup was if you were a member of the PKI. And the PKI had three million members plus over 14 million members of affiliated associations, so you had more chance really of being arrested than of not being arrested. But Hugh had no association with the PKI. Why would they arrest Hugh?

What gave me a cold feeling in the pit of my stomach was the sentence, "food and medicine remain grossly inadequate inside the prisons and camps."

Thursday 10th August 1972

Maria came round. I asked her why she thought Hugh might have been arrested. She said he applied for a visa as a tourist but he would have had "journalist" on his papers. He obviously got into the country alright but if his papers had been checked while he was travelling to Mt Salak, they might have detained him as a foreign journalist without a visa. Is that worse or better than being suspected of being a Communist, I wonder? And we still don't really know if he isn't lying somewhere on the side of Mount Salak.

Maria asked if I'd taken some elephants round to her friend, Alison, yet, so that she could decide if she wanted to sell them in her shop. My mind for a moment couldn't make the leap from Hugh being arrested to someone wanting to sell my elephants. I told Maria I couldn't think about anything else except Hugh at the moment, so she said, okay, she'd take them. Which ones did I want to go? She's like a steam roller. I don't think she can still be in love with Hugh really. If she were, would she be thinking about this sort of thing?

Sunday 15th August 1972

When I think of what might be happening to Hugh at the moment, my tummy curls up tight like a hedgehog.

And all the time, life rolls on.

Jenny wants to come on the Stoke sub Hamdon expedition. She's spending a week with Gwen and can borrow her bike. I wonder how Giles will feel about it. Not that that matters – it's MY expedition, after all.

Tuesday 15th August 1972

This time last year, I baked Hugh a birthday cake. I think it was the worst cake that ever was! The icing was supposed to be pale blue but it came out more like navy blue, and the whole thing was lopsided.

I took it round to Hugh's flat with candles and matches, and we drew the curtains on the sun and sat on the floor in the semi-dark. The candles flickered and Hugh was quiet for a minute. Then he said in his soft Irish voice that the last woman who cooked a birthday cake for him had been his mother when he was seventeen. She died before the year came round again. I touched Hugh's hand and told him I was sorry that I had made him sad, but he said I had brought his mother back to him and that had given him such happiness.

Then we tried to eat the cake. I said I hoped his mother's was better than mine!

Wednesday 16th August 1972

No news from the Foreign Office. How long will it take for the authorities to find out if Hugh is a prisoner over there? I suppose if there are millions and millions of prisoners...

Tomorrow is the Stoke sub Hamdon expedition. I don't want to go away in case there is news but Maria said it could be weeks before they got back to us (WEEKS!!!) and not to be silly. Giles looked a bit taken aback at first about Jenny joining us, but then said it was fine by him. He asked me how I felt about it, and I said that I was a bit worried I wouldn't be able to drink in the atmosphere if I was talking to Jenny all the time, and he suggested he could always take Jenny off to do something else while I mooched about and kissed walls or whatever I wanted to do.

Alice has made a house for "The Major". She has made it out of a cardboard box and decorated it with Indian beads and sequins. Over the door, she has written, "The Major's House", and when I went round to Broomy

Hill last night, "The Major" was standing in the doorway of his house, looking rather pleased with himself. Apparently, her friend, Emily, was very happy with her elephant, and Alice is going to build an extension to her elephant house so that "The Major" can have a visitor.

I have taken the basket off "Klambi" as it would be awkward on the train. Mum has lent me her haversack. It is all packed ready for tomorrow. Jenny, Giles and I are meeting at the station.

Giles is bringing: two puncture kits, a bicycle pump, a first aid box, a stash of cash which he is going to store in one of his socks, change for a telephone box, a fire blanket (?!), a railway timetable, and a notebook containing telephone numbers of Stoke sub Hamdon surgery, the Fleur de Lis pub, his dentist, his bank etc. etc. Good grief! We'll be back on Friday evening! I thought *I* was meant to be the worrier of the expedition.

Thursday night – 17th August 1972

Dear Gwen

Here I am at last in the place where Flo's Mac spent four happy years as Medical Assistant to Dr Walter from 1890-94. This is where Flo and her friend, Carrie Langdon, were shown around by someone called Edith on 19th August 1897 – 74 years ago. Flo must have known that Mac used to live here but she doesn't mention it in her diary at all. I wonder if the whole cycling expedition from Torquay to Bristol was an excuse to see the place where Mac had been living a few years before. She is a girl who keeps her own counsel.

My bedroom window looks out onto the main street, and if I lean out, I can see the top of North Street – the street where Mac lived. Giles' bedroom faces the back garden and Ham Hill. There is a whopping great wall in the garden which doesn't connect to anything. It's where they used to play Fives. Apparently, in the 1700s they wanted to discourage people from bashing balls against the walls of the church, and so they built a Fives Wall for them behind the pub. I've never seen anything like it. The pub itself dates back to fifteen hundred and something. I love this place.

I expect Jenny will tell you all about her farm B&B down in North Street. It was a shame they didn't have a room for her here at the Fleur de Lis, but she said the people at the farm were very friendly.

The train journey was fun. We had two changes and had to lug our bikes on and off trains in the heat. I was glad I wasn't on my own. Jenny and Giles disagreed about everything but they seemed to enjoy the arguments. I've never known Giles so animated, actually.

We arrived at Pen Mill Station after lunch – a nice old-fashioned little station – probably hasn't changed much since Mac and Flo's time – and cycled through Yeovil, with Giles stopping every ten minutes or so to check the map and Jenny teasing him. It was nice to get out of the town and onto the country road towards Montacute.

My legs were pretty tired by the time we got to Montacute but suddenly on my right I saw the old chapel and recognised it from one of Mac's photos from the 1890s. I was in Mac country! I forgot my tired legs. There was the old school at the entrance to Montacute House – that was one of his pictures too. We turned the corner and on the left was the Church and straight ahead was St Michael's Tower up on the hill – another of Mac's photos. The Montacute cottages are all made of the hamstone quarried on Ham Hill, and they glowed gold in the afternoon sun.

The next village was Mac's, Stoke sub Hamdon – just a mile or two up the road. Cycling along the High Street, I remembered Mac's photo of it from the 1890s, so alive with people and carts and horses. The Fleur de Lis was easy to find. Giles and Jenny left me there booking in while they went off to find Jenny's B&B down North Street.

When I had sorted out the pub, I ran down to meet the Giles and Jenny, hoping to find Dr Walter's house, "The Gables", on the way.

There was what looked like a truly ancient building with buttresses on my left and a great mediaeval archway, but it was called, "The Priory, National Trust", so I carried on. I recognised from Mac's photos the rather imposing Congregational Church with its steeple.

Then I saw it. Opposite a gracious looking old farm house. The Gables. It couldn't possibly have been called anything else other than "The Gables" because it was ALL gables. With loads of little narrow windows. I stood and wondered which window was Mac's. I was actually standing where Mac stood to take his photograph of the house back in the 1890s.

I was imagining a little boy running up to the front door in the middle of the night and banging on it – "Dr Mac! Dr Mac! Come quickly!" and Mac looking out of one of the top windows, grabbing his bag and rushing out – when I heard Giles behind me say, "So this is THE house, is it?"

It was fun wandering around Stoke sub Hamdon for what was left of the afternoon, trying to match up Mac's photos to the places.

We found a path called "Whirligig Lane" – really! – and from there you can just about squint into the garden of "The Gables" through a chink in the wall. I have seen a photo of Dr Walter and Mac standing in that garden.

And in Whirligig Lane, there is a funny old mediaeval well which looks just as it did in 1890, when Mac took a photo of some little children standing next to it.

We found the conduit in the High Street – where people used to get their water, and the inscription, "Now God be thanket ye William Pranket in 1701 caus'd this Watter here to Run" – with William Pranket's house just across the street.

The meal tonight at the Fleur de Lis was fun, too. With Jenny and Giles sparring with each other, there were never any awkward silences. We drank too much wine and got very silly.

Portland Street – Friday night

Back in Hereford again. I'm so glad I went. Jenny was such a fun companion. Thank you for letting me steal her from you for part of her stay. I feel ever so much better.

On Friday morning, I went to have a look at the Priory while Giles and Jenny cycled up the Hill to look at the quarry. I think Giles thought I might like some time on my own. We cycled back to Yeovil after that. Our steeds, as Flo would have called them, all behaved very well, and Jenny has such energy that Giles and I never had to stop and wait for her, even though her bike was older than mine. We were in plenty of time for the train – unlike poor flustered Flo in 1897 who nearly missed hers. Giles saw me home to Portland Street and then cycled all the way out to your bungalow with Jenny to make sure she got back safely. He must have been shattered by the time he got home.

Lots of love

Jane

JANE'S DIARY

Friday 18ᵗʰ August 1972

Got home absolutely shattered but so glad that I went. It was like a little oasis in my life, going away for a couple of days. I still had the worry in my heart, but my head was engaged with all that was going on. I feel better. I was all wound up and now I feel just a little bit released. At the same time, I feel guilty thinking about myself, when I don't know what Hugh might be going through.

The best part of the trip, the part which will stay with me always, was the Friday morning. Giles thought I might like a bit of a wander round the village on my own, so he and Jenny cycled up Ham Hill to look at the quarry. I walked down towards "The Gables" again but this time I didn't reach the house. The gate beneath the mediaeval archway which had been closed before, was now open, revealing a beautiful tithe barn and some other farm buildings in a worse state of repair than the barn, with sheep grazing among the ruined walls. I climbed the worn steps leading up into the Priory, and entered a dark hallway. A door in front of me closed off most of the house to the public, but I went through an open doorway on my right.

The room was open to the elements with swallows zig zagging in and out. It was very quiet. Just the 'tseetsee' of the swallows and the shhing of their wings as they rushed over my head. I stood on the uneven earth floor and listened. There was an ancient dead butterfly on the dusty stone windowsill. It felt as if nothing had moved or changed in that place for hundreds of years. In the opposite wall was another open doorway into an adjoining little room. The floor between this room and the one above had long gone and you could see the upstairs fireplace in the wall. There was a window overlooking the walled Priory garden, but I wasn't tall enough to see out of it without holding onto the windowledge and pulling myself up.

I don't know if Mac ever brought Flo to this village, but if he did, this would have been a place where they could have been alone.

Perhaps they would have watched the swallows, and he would have told her how swallows were once thought to be good at healing because they used celandine to give sight to their young. And she would listen, impressed with his knowledge. He would lead her through to this little room and put his hands round her waist and lift her up onto the dusty stone windowsill. Then she would remonstrate, saying, "Mac – no – I'm too heavy – you'll hurt your back!" But he would smile and take no notice. I could see her sweet face through his eyes, framed against the mullions with the old Priory garden beyond, looking down at him with so much love and trust, and suddenly it was me sitting on that windowsill, and the eyes I was smiling down into were Hugh's. And even though maybe Mac and Flo never married, and even though Hugh and I may never see each other again, that moment felt eternal, as if the four of us would always exist in it, somewhere.

Saturday 19th August 1972

No news.

Maria said Alison from the gift shop wants to sell my elephants. Could I go round and see her? I walked up and down the pavement outside the gift shop three times before actually going in this morning. The door tinkled as I opened it and the woman at the counter looked up and smiled, tilting her head to one side. Alison. She was wearing a bright turquoise scarf tied in some clever way round her head and tons of bright silver jangling beads round her neck and wrists. It's funny how the memories of times when you are scared dig their feet in and stay with you.

Alison really seemed to like my elephants. The price thing was easier than I thought. She asked me how much I wanted to charge for them. I admitted that I hadn't the foggiest, but Alison didn't look at me as if I were a moron. She suggested a price and said how much of a percentage she would take. It was all very easy.

I can't wait to tell Mum and Dad. I expect Dad will want to come down to the shop and haggle with Alison over the price. Well, I shan't let him. I'm not doing it for a living. I'm going to get such a kick out of seeing my elephants on those shelves among all the expensive items.

Monday 21st August 1972

No news.

I wandered past Alison's shop at lunchtime and casually looked to see if there were still three elephants on the shelf. There were. Then I wandered past again just to make sure. The third time, Alison came into view from the back of the shop and waved to me. I waved nonchalantly and made a quick exit. I've arranged to meet Mum for coffee in Chadd's tomorrow. Afterwards I am going to surprise her with a visit to see my elephants in situ.

Tuesday 22nd August 1972

I am SO mad! When I got home tonight I threw my cushions all round the room.

I took Mum and showed her my elephants in Alison's shop at lunchtime. That was fine. I could tell she was awfully pleased and excited for me. It was lovely. She gave me a big hug when I left her to go back to work and she said she was proud of me. But I just happened to walk past the shop on my way home and saw that one of the elephants had gone. She went back and bought it. I know she did. It's just the sort of annoying, condescending thing she...

I take it all back. Alison was just at the door, telling me that she has sold my first elephant – to a man who runs an Indian restaurant.

I must ring Mum from the phone box on the corner and let her know.

I have started a new elephant. She is called "Jenny", and she is going to be a confident, chirpy little elephant with custard-coloured ears. I shall throw into her all the optimism I can rake up, and then Hugh will be safe and come home.

Wednesday 23rd August 1972

No news of Hugh.

Alison has sold another of my elephants. I went round as she was putting the "Closed" notice on the door. She said to stay and talk to her while she tidied up. She asked me how I made my elephants and was surprised when I said I invented my own patterns. I said it was like anything – after you've done it lots of times, it gets easy. Then she said,

"Could you tell me how you do it – step by step?"

So I did. When I finished, she asked if I had done any teaching – she thought I would be good at it, that I made it clear and simple. Nobody ever said that to me before.

Thursday 24th August 1972

No news.

I was just reading through the Amnesty International report again (why do I torture myself?) when the doorbell went. It was Alison from the gift shop. She's starting up a craft group. She's going to advertise through her shop and invite people to come along for weekly sessions. She's calling it the "Crafts for Christmas Group", with people making their own Christmas presents, and she wants me to teach them to sew an elephant!!! Me!

I said I would think about it.

I cycled out to see Gwen at Burghill this evening. It has been a dull day but the clouds started to clear at about 8 and we sat in her garden among the scent of roses and watched the remaining wisps of cloud grow pink in the sunset. I brought a bottle of wine in "Klambi's" basket. I had a glorious couple of hours talking about Hugh. I told her about Alison's idea too and that I was going to say no. She asked me why and I said I couldn't really concentrate on anything but Hugh at the moment. She asked what I thought Hugh would say about that. And what Flo would have done.

Friday 25th August 1972

No news.

I called in at the gift shop during my lunch hour, and told Alison I would do her "Crafts for Christmas Group". She was ever so pleased. She said she would get them to bring their own materials if I would give her a list. It's going to be on a Tuesday night in the stock room above the shop. She's got some takers already. She must have been confident I would say yes.

Giles asked me at work today what the situation was with Hugh. I told him. He said he was sorry. Ever since we went to Stoke sub Hamdon, I have felt he was on the verge of saying something. I don't want him to say it.

My Amnesty International report is all soggy. Diana Ross has a new Number 1 this week – "I'm Still Waiting." I went out and bought it at lunchtime. Big mistake. I have been playing it over and over this evening and weeping buckets.

Saturday 26th August 1972

No news. Giles asked if I would have Alice for the afternoon so I took her to see *An Elephant Called Slowly*. It wasn't as good as *Born Free*, but it was about elephants and both Alice and I are into those.

Gwen was very pleased I had agreed to do the craft sessions. She says the important thing is to prepare properly and to know exactly what was going to happen in each lesson. She says if you are prepared, you feel confident, and that comes over to your students. "Time spent in reconnaissance is seldom wasted," her commanding officer in the FANY used to say. Gwen was a geography teacher after the Great War, so she knows what she's talking about. I told her how I felt Flo was pushing me to do it. We talked about Flo's cycling expedition all the way from Devon to Bristol. Gwen thinks Flo wanted to see where Mac had worked before they met, and that it was knowing that Mac loved her which gave her the courage and the impetus to make that journey. Gwen said I should keep thinking about how much Hugh loves me.

My newest elephant, "Jenny" is nearly finished. The elephants are selling quite well and Alison is keen not to run out so I need to make more.

I had a letter from the real Jenny, saying how much she had enjoyed the Stoke sub Hamdon expedition. She is coming to stay with Gwen again in September/October, and she wants to go cycling with me and Giles. I would have thought she would have seen enough of him last week from the way they were arguing!

I have been mentally kissing Hugh's ears. He used to stand very still while I did it, almost as if he was holding his breath. I had to go on tiptoe. He has such perfect ears – like those on a Greek statue. Not particularly small (because everything about Hugh is large) but nicely formed.

Gwen thinks I should tell my family about Hugh. She says the longer I leave it, the more difficult it will be. Hmmm!

Sunday 27th August 1972

Giles turned up on my doorstep tonight with a bottle of wine. We sat and talked for a bit about work. The silences got longer and eventually he said what he had come to say – that he was in love with me and wanted to marry me, and I got on well with Alice and his mother, didn't I? I said I was very flattered but that I was in love with Hugh. Giles was quiet for a moment, and then he said, well, if the worst happened and Hugh didn't come back, would I think about what he had said?

He made it all sound so cold blooded. As if he had carefully weighed up all the pros and cons. I didn't know how to react. Perhaps he's still in love with his wife, but he feels he ought to provide a mother for Alice as his mother is getting on. The thought of living in that house with his mother watching me trying to be a mother to Alice makes my blood run cold.

The Giles I saw tonight was quite different from the kind-hearted, funny, bossy Giles I know at work. I dread going into work tomorrow.

No news. I feel so powerless. I went to Mass again this morning and lit another candle for Hugh.

Monday 28th August 1972

NEWS! I'm so excited. I can hardly write. Maria came to see me at work. She had been running and was breathless. I took her into the Gestetner cupboard, and it was there, with the smell of Gestetner fluid and dusty paper, that she told me the Foreign Office have confirmed that Hugh is in Salemba prison in Jakarta. The Foreign Office is going to try to get him released. Whatever he is having to put up with, it will soon all be over and he will be home!

After Maria had gone, I found myself sobbing uncontrollably in the cupboard, trying not to be heard, and then I went back to my desk and made mistakes for the rest of the day. I couldn't tell Giles or Jeanie or anyone. I just wanted to keep it to myself for a bit.

Tuesday 29th August 1972

After the news yesterday, I hardly worried about the craft class at all. Was I glad I had prepared it all at the weekend, though!

I went round to the shop early to help Alison shift the boxes around up in the storeroom to give us a bit more room.

The first to arrive was an elderly lady who had been dropped off at the door with her heavy, ancient sewing machine. I lugged it up the stairs for her with her thanking me profusely on every step. She said she had made clothes in the past but never toys. Alison took her details while I went down to let some more in.

We had six. Their faces and names are all a bit of a blur at the moment, but there was the elderly lady, a woman with her rather sulky daughter, a girl with sad eyes, delicate features and a foreign accent, a very bouncy, hippy type girl with loads of beads, bright, wide, flowery flares and an embroidered waistcoat, and another girl who obviously wasn't too bright. She was brought by her father who made a speedy escape. Only the last two didn't have machines as the mother shared hers with her daughter, so with mine and Alison's, we were fine.

Alison did a little spiel to start us off and then got everyone talking, saying what they had done in the sewing line, if anything, and who they intended their finished elephant for. The elderly lady was very deaf but luckily was quite open and jokey about it. The sulky girl didn't say a word. Her mother answered every question Alison put to her. The hippy girl, on the other hand, never stopped talking, while the "not too bright" one just sat and smiled. Her name was Felicity and I was a bit worried as to whether she would cope, but although she needed quite a bit of help threading the machine, she managed to cut out her pattern quite well, with great concentration and the tip of her tongue showing between her lips. I think she will be okay.

I think perhaps it all went well because I had this bubble of joy inside me. That made everything fun and people responded to it.

I am looking forward to the next one. But none of this matters when I think about Hugh – surely there is something we can be doing? I'm desperate to write to him.

Thursday 31st August 1972

The chain on my locket broke today. I just sank onto the floor and wept. I have worn my locket every day since Hugh fastened it round my neck last Christmas. Inside is a picture of Hugh on one side and Granny on the other. They are smiling into each other's eyes. I wish Hugh had known her. She would have loved him.

Saturday 2nd September 1972

Maria says the Foreign Office are trying to find out if we can write to Hugh while they are sorting his release. If food is scarce, perhaps we could send him some. Why does everything take so long?

I told Giles today that we know where Hugh is now and are trying to get him home. He said he was glad. And then, tonight, he turned up on my doorstep again.

I was curled up in my pyjamas and dressing gown this evening, watching *The Benny Hill Show*, when I heard the pathetic croak of my non-functioning doorbell. It was Giles, standing there with a bottle of wine in his hand. My heart sank.

"Don't worry," he said. "I haven't come to pester you – I just wondered if we could talk."

But he didn't talk properly, not for ages. Eventually, after a glass or two and some chatting about work and my "Jenny" elephant, the conversation ground to a halt. The room was very quiet, just every now and then the purr of a car going by on Portland Street. We drank our wine and watched Benny Hill silently rushing about on the turned down TV. My instinct was to break the silence but I took a leaf out of Gwen's book and held on. And Giles suddenly started talking about his wife, Susan, who died six years ago when Alice was born.

"Susan used to like that programme," he said.

"Did she?"

"I used to pull her leg about it."

I asked him how they had met and he said it was while they were at Uni – they belonged to the same folk club. They were at one of those gatherings where people take it in turns to get up and perform. He said in those days, he was very shy and had no self-confidence at all (hard to imagine) He would never have got up to sing on his own, but Susan did, and the first time he heard her voice he fell for her right away.

Giles was looking through the TV screen now, rather than at it, and was a long way away. I kept as quiet as I could and let him talk. He told me that they married only a few months after they had met, much to the consternation of their parents. Giles was fresh from an all male, very establishment type boarding school. Susan was the very opposite. In spite of her gentle appearance, she was passionate about politics and all for challenging the status quo in defence of the underdog. She took part in the first Aldermaston March back in 1958. I should imagine she didn't go down too well with Giles' parents!

Susan converted Giles to her ideas and he enthusiastically joined her in anti-this and anti-that demonstrations. I couldn't quite imagine it and said so. He said one of the awful things about losing her was that he lost that part of himself – the person he was when he was with her. He said there was an anti-Vietnam demonstration in London a couple of years ago. He should have been there, but he'd just watched it on television. And then he started to cry. I'd never seen a man cry before, not even my brother. I didn't know what to do. If it had been anyone else, I would have given him a hug. In the end, I just squeezed his hand, and he squeezed mine back and shook out his immaculate handkerchief, ironed by Vanessa I should imagine.

He said it was the first time he had talked to anyone about Susan – in six years!

Susan was only 27 when she died – just four years older than I am now. They were married in 1958.

I felt so sorry for him. I wish he had someone.

Sunday 3rd September 1972

Maria came round. She had heard again from the Foreign Office. Apparently, the authorities had been on the lookout for Hugh's guide – a man called Adika. Someone had denounced him as a Communist sympathiser. When they found Hugh in his company and discovered he was a journalist (or so they thought from his papers) they arrested him too and so he ended up in a political prison rather than a criminal one.

I said, "That's a good thing then." But Maria said no, the political prisons were worse than the criminal ones. She said political prisoners were not allowed to have any knowledge of the outside world – no newspapers or television. They were denied any means of writing. But they were allowed to receive food parcels, and extra bedding etc. and the Foreign Office are contacting the Indonesian Red Cross to get some supplies to him.

So, I can't write to him. I had so hoped I might be able to get a letter to him. But perhaps when he gets a Red Cross parcel with his name on it, he will realise that we know he is there and that we are doing our best to get him out.

I don't know how Hugh will cope without being able to draw or paint.

Monday 4th September 1972

I woke up this morning in the middle of a lovely dream about Hugh, but a second after my eyes opened it disappeared, and I spent ages trying to recapture it. I wonder why I always have good dreams about him and never nightmares. I'm tempted to think that it's because we are so closely linked that I would know if he was in a bad way, but it is probably just because my mind can't cope with the thought of his being cold or hungry or in pain, or lonely, even when I'm asleep.

Tuesday 5th September 1972

Maria says the Red Cross have arranged for a parcel to be delivered to Salemba prison. What wouldn't I give to see him open it?! Still no news of his release date.

Session two of the craft group under my belt. I had planned quite a lot for them to do. I moved from table to table to make sure they were doing it right. Alison had all her time cut out looking after Felicity. There was an awful lot of argument going on at the mother/daughter table! I think I might try to separate them next week. I just caught Serena (the hippy girl) trying to sew her shapes together without leaving an opening for the stuffing. At her age I would have been mortified to be caught in a mistake but she just thought it was funny. She has such confidence in herself.

We stopped for a coffee break at half time. Last week, Alison suggested they bring something they had made previously. The elderly lady – Mavis – had brought in a tiny pair of bootees she had knitted for her baby great granddaughter. Of course, everyone asked her about the baby – when was it born? – what was it called? – and she looked very sad and said that there had been a family argument and she hadn't been allowed to see the baby. It wasn't her fault. It was something to do with the in-laws. I think it touched all of us to watch her absent-mindedly stroking those little knitted bootees. Serena was full of indignation. The mother of the sulky girl talked about other families she knew who didn't get on. Felicity patted Mavis' knee. Even the sulky girl looked interested. Only Kartika – the foreign looking lady – looked rather distant and didn't join in.

After the break, they had to iron their elephants-to-be and then embroider the eyelashes, using blanket stitch. This was easy for Mavis but not for some of the others. We got Felicity to sew on buttons instead. Mavis was finished before any of the others and started stuffing the body and ears of her elephant.

I walked up Aylestone Hill afterwards to tell Mum and Dad about it. I could see they were amazed and they both looked so pleased and excited for me. I think they had become resigned to the fact that I was not going to do anything with my life, just hide from the world. I never thought I would be able to do something to make them proud of me.

If only Hugh were safe and here with me now, I would be utterly content.

Felicity calls us the "Crafty Christmas Club" and it seems to have stuck.

Wednesday 6th September 1972

Awful news about the Israeli Olympic team being kidnapped and killed. And more British soldiers have been killed and injured in Ireland. I asked Dad the other day what he thought about the situation over there and he said he was glad to be out of the army. I'm going to give up watching the news.

My parents have asked me if I want to go away on holiday with them next week. Of course, I can't go anywhere at the moment. They think I am just being negative. I am going to have to tell them what's going on.

I cycled out to Dinedor Hill on my own this evening to watch the sunset. I had this crazy idea that I could wave to Hugh from the top of the hill and he would know. I've never done anything like that before. I felt Flo was very near. It was as if she was cycling behind me and if I just turned my head, we could smile at each other. I got there with the sun was turning bright red and as it sank into the mist on the horizon, it made the mist a warm red colour too. By morning, that mist will have covered everything, ready to clear away by about ten o'clock, and another lovely day will have started. I had to pedal like mad to get home before dark.

Thursday 7th September 1972

I've done it! Actually, I did what Flo did when she wanted to tell her parents about being engaged to Mac: I told Mum, and asked her to tell Dad. I thought it would be easier to talk at Chadd's than at my parents' house. I never ask Mum to my bedsit. I can't bear the pained expression in her eyes!

I started off saying how pleased I was that they had invited me to go on holiday with them and then explained why I couldn't go. I'd rehearsed it all for hours beforehand but people never say what you expect them to, so the conversation didn't go as I had imagined. She didn't say a word to start with, just sipped her coffee. It was unnerving, to say the least. I think she was probably thinking, "Oh God! How am I going to tell Bob?!"

Then she said, "This chap, he says he's going to leave his wife?" And you could tell she was thinking, "My poor idiot of a daughter – the oldest trick in the book!" When I told her that I was quite friendly with Maria who knew all about it, she started to look more relaxed. I could see she was dying to know whether Hugh and I had slept together so I just came right out with it and said we hadn't, and that seemed to put the whole thing on a higher plane for her. She said she wished I had told her earlier – she didn't like to think of how I had struggled with all this since the beginning of the year. Dear Mum! You just never know with people, do you?

She didn't know much about the political prisoner situation in Indonesia but she said she was sure it would all be okay and I'd be seeing Hugh again soon.

I felt so relieved that I'd told her. I hadn't realised how much it was weighing on me. I wonder what Daddy will say.

Friday 8th September 1972

Mum took me out for lunch to tell me about Dad's reaction. She said at first things were a bit sticky but in the end he was fine about it. She said he was upset for me because of the present situation, but felt that once Hugh is home and, as he put it, the situation is "regulated", that Hugh will be quite a catch for me. Phew! I think they are both relieved that there is a chance I might be – A. not single for the rest of my life, and B. solvent.

She asked me if Hugh was very attractive. I think she was imagining a sort of Casanova, irresistible to women. He might have a trail of broken-hearted women in his wake but he wouldn't realise it. He treats women like friends. I asked him once if there had been anyone since

Maria. He said no, the only thing he had been passionate about had been his work. He thought he had been waiting for me. He asked me about my boyfriends. I told him I had had a crush on a nun at school, and been in love with Sir Walter Raleigh, and Steed from *The Avengers*, and John Lennon. He put his hands gently on either side of my face and said, "Sure, I should go away and give you time to grow up!"

Back at work this afternoon, I finished indexing the Chave family papers and started on Mac's trunk. I was hoping that I might find some clue to what happened – why he and Flo never married.

I found an envelope full of newspaper cuttings in the trunk. There was a report of his leaving presentation at Burghill Asylum in June 1902. They gave him a solid silver cup with his initials on it, a handsome black marble and bronze clock and an "illuminated address" signed by around 100 members of staff. They certainly knew how to throw leaving parties in those days. The last secretary who left our place had a box of chocolates and some flowers, was told she had been fun to work with, and thought herself lucky.

The chaplain who was supposed to have given Mac's presentation was busy at a parish meeting. He had sent a letter, expressing his "warm appreciation of Dr McCutchan's kindness to himself and the staff generally, and his sincere wishes for his future welfare."

Mac replied (and I love the way they quoted whole conversations in those days – did they take them down in shorthand?) that he felt deeply indebted to them all, and Hereford would always have for him many pleasant associations (applause). During his term of office, he had endeavoured to be uniformly kind but when in the execution of his duties he had to appear unkind, he then endeavoured to be as kind as unkindness would permit. He certainly hoped that the clock would tick away pleasant hours for him. At any rate, it would always recall to his mind the many happy days he had spent at Burghill. Then they sang "Auld Lang Syne".

I didn't have time to look any further today. I wonder where he went on to.

I am designing another elephant. I don't know if it is male or female, or what its name is going to be, which is unusual for me. I generally have it all planned out.

I was glad to have Mac's leaving address to cheer me up today because I was upset that I couldn't "hear" Hugh's voice in my head. You can recall someone's face with a photograph, but unless it is recorded, a voice is lost for ever once it has gone from your memory.

Sunday 10th September 1972

Last night I dreamt I heard Hugh's voice and this morning I could hear him as clearly as anything saying my name. It was a gift.

I cycled over to Gwen's this afternoon. She made me a cup of tea with real tea and a teapot and a strainer – the works. I love watching her in the kitchen. She never rushes. She takes care over things. The only time I have ever seen her flustered is when I first met her and she was trying to cope with the new decimal coins.

Gwen said Jenny has applied for a job at St Mary's in Burghill – Mac's old asylum! If she gets it, she'll be staying with her grandmother until she finds her own place. I am so pleased for them both. It will make such a difference to Gwen's life, having Jenny there.

Monday 11th September 1972

I have found an envelope in Mac's trunk full of "Testimonials". He applied for a post in the new asylum at Talgarth in February 1902. This was four years after he and Flo got engaged. The doctor giving his reference says he has the highest opinion of his personal qualities – he is intensely interested in the work, upright in his dealings and "has shown much tact in dealing with those under his authority". He didn't get the Talgarth job, though. He ended up in Cambridgeshire. I found a programme for a Musical and Dramatic Entertainment – Christmas 1902 – at Fulbourn Asylum near Cambridge. Mac is in the lead role.

Cambridge is an awfully long way away from Hereford and Flo. I wonder how she felt about it.

At least they could write to each other.

Tuesday 12th September 1972

Still no news.

Another Crafty Christmas evening. They all arrived around the same time and I could hear them chatting to each other as they climbed the stairs, sulky girl's mother (Janet) helping Mavis with her machine.

Felicity was surprisingly good at blind stitch. We had put Janet and her daughter on separate tables. Janet seemed a bit taken aback but Sulky Girl looked pleased. They all work really well as a group now. They chatter away together and compare elephants. It's lovely. The only quiet one is Kartika, but I found out why tonight.

During tea break, Serena asked her if her name meant anything. I think only Serena would have done it, because there is something contained about Kartika which makes you shy of approaching her. She looked a little surprised, and said quietly it meant "Shining Star" in Indonesian.

The others were all saying how lovely that was, and then Serena asked her how long she had been in the UK, and she said how she had had to escape from Java after the troubles in 1965. I nearly dropped my mug. I wanted to ask her so much but couldn't in front of everyone.

At the end of the evening, after Serena had stuffed her tail inside out by mistake and sewn her tail fringe onto the elephant's head, causing Felicity to giggle uncontrollably, I went over to Kartika's table where she was quietly packing away her stuff. I asked her if she would like to come over to my flat for a coffee tomorrow. She looked very surprised, and so I said I had a friend in Java. Her face actually seemed to freeze with fear for a moment and then, I suppose, I must have looked harmless because she nodded and asked for my address. She's coming round about eight. I am frightened of what she might tell me, but anything to bring Hugh closer.

Wednesday 13th September 1972

Kartika has just gone. It took her a while to relax and talk freely but in the end she did, and I think she found it a help to talk to someone about what had happened to her.

I can't imagine what it must have been like to have lived through that. They didn't only arrest people suspected of being Communists – they arrested their whole family and anyone connected with them. If you heard them coming for you, you had to either watch your family being arrested or tortured and killed, or accuse your neighbours and friends of being Communist sympathisers and hope they'd go off and leave you alone. What a horrible choice to have to make! Kartika said she wouldn't go into detail of the ways they killed people. It was too awful.

Her father was a journalist and was arrested. The men came back for her mother and herself one night and her mother told her to make a run for it out of the back door. She never saw her mother again. Kartika made her way to a relative's house who managed to get her out of the country. A friend of her father's lives in Hereford and that is how she comes to be here. She works as a cleaner and shares a flat with another refugee.

I told her about Hugh. She said there was a good chance the Foreign Office could negotiate Hugh's release. She thought England had good connections with the Suharto regime because President Suharto was anti-Communist, and both England and America were worried about the threat of Communism.

The crazy thing is that she thinks she might know the family of Hugh's guide. I asked her if she might write to them to see if she can find out any more. She was a bit dubious, not wanting to get them into trouble, but said she would try.

I wonder if Hugh has a cell to himself, if he has contact with other people. I wonder if anyone there speaks English.

I have been reading Mac's references. They all say how kind he was. I think perhaps Hugh is Mac reincarnated. He is the kindest person ever. Not many people round here know that he is "HOD", the famous cartoonist. He keeps away from publicity. He's the unknown person on the bus who cheers up the lonely old lady, or buys an ice cream in the park for the child who has dropped hers on the path. He's the person who makes everyone laugh in the lift when it stops between floors. He's the person who convinces a lonely, timid girl that she is lovable.

Wednesday 13th September 1972

No news.

I had a letter from Jenny this morning. She's very excited about her new job at Burghill. She doesn't start for a few weeks but says there is a lecture there on the 23rd and would I like to go with her? It would be fantastic to actually go inside the building where Mac used to work. Of course I will say yes.

Another thing that keeps me sane is planning the Crafty Christmas sessions. Third one tomorrow. They have to sew up their ear openings with blind stitch which should give an invisible join if they do it right. Then they have to sort out their tails. Flo would have no trouble with it, and I'm sure Mac would be jolly good at all this surgical stuff. I think he probably had to do a lot of post-mortems.

Friday 15th September 1972

Giles has asked if I would take Alice out again tomorrow afternoon. I thought we might wander round the town pretending to be secret agents. I did wonder if Giles might still be hoping that he and I might get together. I talked to Gwen about it and she thinks he may have reached a point where he is ready to fall in love again but hasn't yet. She thinks he is just testing the water with me but doesn't realise it.

Saturday 16th September 1972

Today is my birthday. Mum and Dad and Rob are away on a climbing expedition. They rang me at work yesterday to say happy birthday. I have had a good day with plenty of company but I can't help thinking of this time last year when Hugh was with me. Last summer, wherever you went, they were playing "Maggie May" by Rod Stewart. I remember sitting in the flat in Cantilupe Street with my head on Hugh's shoulder, listening to "Maggie May", and being aware that I was, in that moment, utterly content.

I spent this morning planting secret clues and instructions inside the crevices of walls etc. round the town. Then Giles arrived with Alice about 2 p.m. He had brought me a birthday card. I was glad he didn't give me anything else. You can give a card to anyone.

Alice and I did have such fun in the town! We surreptitiously found and read my notes and followed the instructions which took us all over the place. Then I bought us both some cheapo dark glasses from Woolworths and we sat in a café with our dark glasses on, staring furtively at the passers-by. I showed her my cartridge pen which could shoot out a cloud of knock out gas, and she showed me her hairclip which was really a two-way radio. When Giles came to collect her from Portland Street, she was busy turning my sofa into a bed and back again.

While Giles was there, Jenny suddenly turned up! She had descended upon Gwen unexpectedly as a surprise for the weekend. She chatted for ages and then we got hungry and Giles said why didn't he go and get fish and chips? So, we all feasted on fish and chips and then played Scrabble, Jenny and Giles disagreeing on every word. Alice's spelling was better than either of theirs. Giles suggested the three of us going cycling tomorrow morning. We're going to Wormelow Tump. No reason really. We just like the name.

It was good to have a few hours' distraction from worrying about Hugh.

Sunday 17th September 1972

The day started fine for our cycle ride this morning, but half way to Wormelow Tump, it just tipped down. We were all wet through by the time we got there. We had our picnic in the church porch. On the way back we could hardly see our way for the rain. Jenny was careering fearlessly down a steep hill along a fairly narrow road, with Giles and myself picking our way behind a bit more sedately, when a sheep suddenly appeared right in front of her and she swerved and disappeared into a gateway. Giles put on a violent spurt, braked noisily and threw himself off his bike. I could hear him yelling out – was she alright?

By the time I got there, he was helping her to her feet and she was laughing, but I could see he had been really worried. For a moment, all was sweetness and light between them but then Giles started saying she had been cycling too fast for the conditions and she really ought to slow down the rest of the way, and of course Jenny wasn't going to be told what to do. I think she knew he was right really, and that made her crosser. She got on her bike and rushed off in front of us but after a while she relented and stopped to wait.

Gwen had invited us all back for lunch, and she insisted we all had hot baths and a change of clothes. It was so funny watching Giles cycling away with Gwen's deceased husband's trousers flapping half way up his legs. I hope he didn't meet any of his clients on his way home.

Thursday 21st September 1972

At last! Good news at last!

Maria has heard from the Foreign Office. They have got the Indonesian government to agree to Hugh's release.

It's like a hundred birthday presents at once. I was asking her – when, when, when?! She said they are releasing a lot of prisoners at the end of September and Hugh will be among them. Only 9 days!

I can't believe it. After months and months of agony. I went round to tell Gwen. Funny, how I go to her rather than to my mother. She got out a bottle of wine and we toasted Hugh till it was all gone, and I wobbled home on "Klambi". I did ring Mum from the phone box, though, and she sounded awfully pleased for me.

Gwen asked if I would still go to Burghill with Jenny on Saturday. I said of course I would and that I would write and tell her all about it.

Friday 22nd September 1972

Never has the time gone so slowly. 8 days to go. I keep imagining Hugh will get ill and not make it to the 30th. Kartika came round again to say she had tried writing to the family of Hugh's guide but not had any reply.

Tomorrow evening is Jenny's lecture at St Mary's Hospital. I feel as if I will be visiting Mac and he will be there to comfort me.

I was remembering today when Hugh and I took the bus to Hay-on-Wye. He kissed me in every nook and cranny in every bookshop. For me, now, the musty scent of old books is inextricably mixed with desire and the smell of pipe tobacco.

24th September 1972

Dear Gwen

Such a day yesterday!

I felt almost breathless, stepping over the threshold of St Mary's with Jenny. And of course, Jenny was thrilled to be in the place where she will soon be working.

I've seen old photographs of the inside of St Mary's when it was Burghill Lunatic Asylum – the nurses looking very proper in their long skirts and aprons, standing around in rooms which looked polished and clean but dark. It's all quite different now. There's still a bit of an institution feel about the place with green paint everywhere and rather a Brussels sprouty smell, but it's airy and there's a friendly atmosphere. Actually, though, we didn't see much of it as we were immediately directed towards the nurses' quarters, where people were milling about and finding their seats in a little hall. Jenny marched me up to the front. I felt a complete fraud among all those medical people.

Then the speaker came in – his name was David Clark, and I got the shock of my life when he introduced himself. I suppose I hadn't told Jenny about Mac moving on from Burghill to Fulbourn so she hadn't realised what it would mean to me. You see, David Clark was the Medical Superintendent of Fulbourn Mental Hospital!!!

He started out at Fulbourn in the 1950s, at a time when it was all locked wards and doom and gloom, and he completely changed the place round so that now it is all open and the patients and nurses work together. Wouldn't Mac have got on well with him? It was exactly what he would have loved to have done himself if he had had free rein.

Dr Clark was lovely. He spoke in words even I could understand. He was so enthusiastic about his work – it almost made me want to work in mental health. The nurses asked loads of questions afterwards and the room was buzzing. He didn't go into much detail about the history of Fulbourn before he started working there, though, and that was what I wanted to know. What had happened to Mac? How long had he worked there?

But I DID manage to talk to him afterwards. Jenny and I had got ourselves a cup of tea and Jenny had got into conversation with a couple of the nurses. As I stood there, drinking my tea, I realised that David Clark was in a little group nearby. I heard him say he was going to get something from his car and I made after him like a greyhound. As he opened the boot of his car, I squeaked, "Excuse me!" and he sort of leapt into the air a bit.

I explained that I was interested in a doctor who used to work at Fulbourn in the early 1900s and did he know anything about that time? He asked me for the name, and when I told him, he said, "Oh yes, I remember reading about him in the records – poor chap!"

And, oh, poor Mac died in 1906! Dr Clark said there was a typhoid epidemic at the asylum the previous summer. Mac did a brilliant job, taking over the asylum when Dr Rogers, the Medical Superintendent, caught typhoid, but the strain of the whole thing ruined his health and he died of heart problems the following summer. He was only 47. Dr Clark said he had read a report by the two doctors in charge of the investigation as to the source of the epidemic, and they had written a glowing report about how Mac had dealt with it.

I really feel I have got to know him through Flo's diary, and through his references and papers. He was kind to people who had no one else to look out for them, and he loved music and dancing, and amateur dramatics, and cycling, and birds and the countryside. He worked hard. And most of all, he loved Flo with an intensity which never wavered all through the years.

I could cry for Flo. She waited for over ten years for him. And then, I suppose, she waited another sixty years or more because she never married. Neither shall I, if Hugh doesn't come back. Sorry – that slipped out. Against the rules. But it's odd that it is now when I know that Hugh is on his way back to me, that I learn Flo has lost her Mac for ever. It's almost as if she has let Mac go so that I can have Hugh.

I think I am going round the bend!

Love

Jane

Monday 25ᵗʰ September 1972

I lost a sock this morning. Hugh would get very Irish when he lost anything. I never actually heard him say, "Begorrah!", but there would be plenty of "Whisht now!" and "BeJasus!" and "Would you look at that?" It would make me laugh. I wonder if we will still be able to laugh together when he gets home, or if what he has been through will alter him so that he won't be able to laugh any more. I'm so scared that he will need more than I will know how to give him. He will be like a soldier coming back from the war, having experienced things I can't imagine.

Maria says the British Ambassador will meet him outside the prison and then he will be flown back to RAF Fairford. It has been so difficult, being his "girlfriend" rather than his wife. Maria says she feels it will be best if I keep in the background – she says Hugh will need to disappear with me for a bit to have peace and quiet, and she doesn't want the press hounding us. She is so calm about it all.

I asked if that meant I shouldn't go with her to meet him at RAF Fairford. She said, "Don't be silly! Of course you're coming." Thank God! I couldn't face sitting here in Hereford and not being there to watch him getting off the plane.

Tuesday 26ᵗʰ September 1972

Crafty Christmas this evening. Their elephants are very nearly finished. Having only just tackled blind stitch last week, some of them were nervous about using it again when inserting the tail into the opening of their elephant's rear end. It's a bit tricky to do. Alison helped Felicity and I helped Kartika, but Serena got into a bit of a pickle with hers. Mavis and Kim hardly need any help at all but Serena tends to rush at things. Her ears got sewn on in the wrong place and had to be redone.

During the coffee break, Kartika came over and asked me quietly whether there was any news of Hugh and I told her that he is going to be released any day now. Serena was close by and was listening and asked who Hugh was, and then the others realised something was going on so I told them all about it. They were really sympathetic and excited. Kim and her daughter couldn't get over the fact I knew "HOD". Kartika looked a bit overwhelmed at first but then I think quite enjoyed the fact that she had known about Hugh before the others. I couldn't have shared it with them all before, but now that I know he will soon be home, it's okay.

Next week he might – will – be home.

PART 3 – LETTERS

Herefordshire Record Office
Harold Street
Hereford

22nd September 1972

Miss Jane Brown
The Basement Flat
Albert House
Portland Street
Hereford
Herefordshire

Dear Jane

Re: The Chave Family Papers

Thank you very much indeed for all your work on the Chave family papers. Your index will be invaluable.

The Council has been doing some work in the attic of Moor House and a tin has been found containing some letters belonging to Miss Chave which they have passed on to us.

Do drop into the Record Office at any time if you are interested in reading these, but you may feel you have had enough of these records by now!

Many thanks and best wishes

Yours sincerely

Miss E M Jancey

Chief Archivist

Fulbourn Asylum, Cambridgeshire

Wednesday 4th June 1902

My Own Sweet Girl

It has been a long journey but here I am at last in my new quarters – sitting at my desk, feeling rather homesick and lost, like a boy at a new school. The bedroom is tiny, but my study has a comfortable old leather chair, a good fireplace and a desk at which I can write to my Flo. When I have put my bird pictures up on the walls and Scotty the Skeleton on his stand, and photographs of my dear parents and my brothers and sisters on the desk, it will look more homely. I have a richly coloured Indian rug which will cheer up the threadbare carpet. At present, the room seems rather cold and unfriendly. Perhaps it is just that the one person I want to be in it is many miles away.

The evening is still warm. I have opened the window with difficulty – I don't think the previous incumbent (another Scotsman) ever touched it – and the scents of the midsummer night are drifting in. Owls are answering each other in the elm trees. Somewhere, a long way to the west of here, you are perhaps looking out of your bedroom window, seeing the same stars appearing faintly, seeing the same nearly full moon rising above the trees. It is a comfort.

I want to hear from you that you are alright. I cannot bear for you to be unhappy on my account. If I were working at Talgarth, how much closer we should have been to each other this night! But it is no good thinking like that. We must think of this position as one step nearer to our married happiness. We know that we are fortunate, and that there are men and women who have never experienced what we feel for one another.

Give your parents my very best wishes. I hope Billie is being a good boy and has given up escaping.

I have saved one of the sandwiches you gave me and will eat it now. It made me laugh when you whipped them out of your pocket at the last minute and gave them to me through the train window. It was like you! I suppose it is being the eldest of six which makes you so ready to look after people. My eldest sister, Ada, tends to mother us all.

I love you very much, my darling. Always remember that.

Write to me from Devon. Tell me everything. Tell me that you are happy.

My love, always

Mac (SENIOR Assistant Medical Officer!)

For My Flo

When you are to the west of me
You must kiss the sun good day
And send him with the zest of you
To meet me on his way.

When I am to the east of you
I shall watch the sun's last light
And whisper that the least of me
Sends you my love this night.

When sleep's too shy to lie with you
And the sun has vanished quite,
I'll watch the bright night sky with you
And hug you to me tight.

Though always I'm afar from you
And never hand in hand,
I touch the evening star with you
And we together stand.

The world with you is fair anew
Alive with love and grace;
All days and ways that I fare through
Are dearer for your face.

My Ain Dear Flo

You will tell from how I address you that I have been dipping into Rabbie Burns again. I think I told you that my father maintained we were descended from the poet. He was baptised Robert as a result. When my father was sad, and business worried him, we would find him sitting with a book of Burns' poems on his knee.

Well, this place is nothing like Burghill, and the Medical Superintendent is nothing like dear Dr Morrison. The train journey took nearly all day with several changes and a good deal of waiting around on platforms. As every mile passed, I felt ever more strongly that a part of me was missing. The better part, my darling.

A funny old chap met me at Fulbourn Station and managed to pack me, my belongings and my bicycle onto the trap. The tired looking pony trotted up the long sweep of the neat drive, and stopped in front of the central administrative block which is to be my home. If I hadn't known better, I would have imagined I was arriving to stay at some house of quality, but on being shown round the Asylum by Mr Thorne, I soon lost that impression.

Mr Thorne is the Principal Male Attendant. It appears that he is one of the many members of staff who have been here for years. Mr Thorne had been asked to show me round in the absence of the Medical Superintendent, Dr Rogers.

He showed me the men's wards first – some of the men were out working in the fields or in the workshops but a few were just sitting there, being watched by the staff. Then the women's ward. The same dismal-looking clothing. I will spare you the details, my love. Suffice to say that the expressions of resignation and dreariness on their faces were mirrored in the faces of the staff who were caring for these poor souls. Mr Thorne then took me to the airing courts – the exercise yards – where a long string of men and youths, hand in hand, were walking ponderously and in a pitifully aimless fashion, backwards and forwards along one of the paths. Mr Thorne said that it was only by such companionship that they could be persuaded to take any exercise at all.

I hope I can do some good here but it depends upon Dr Rogers' attitude. If he will let me try out some of the ideas Dr Morrison and I put into practice in Burghill, then – well, we'll see.

My darling, this is a poor sort of a love letter. I promise to do better. Do you remember my first letters to you? How correct I was! If we had married four years ago, when we were first engaged to each other, would we by now be a staid wedded couple, with no excitement in our lives? I can't imagine my heart not beating faster when I hear your dear voice, or open an envelope with your letter inside.

Let me know how your father does. I hope the Devon air improves his health. He has always been so kind to me, and he need not have been.

Let me know how you are, dearest.

As fair art thou, my <u>bonnie</u> lass,
So deep in luve am I;
And I will luve thee still, my dear,
Till a' the seas gang dry.
Yours, till a' the seas gang dry
Mac

My Darling Cycling Partner

I am sorry not to have been able to write sooner. My life is unbelievably busy at the moment. Dr Rogers makes the decisions but it seems the Assistant Medical Officer is here to do all the work! Not that Dr Rogers hasn't been very charming and hospitable. He and his sister, Miss Annie Rogers, have asked me to dine with them twice already. The food for the staff is much superior to that given to the inmates. I'm afraid many of these look malnourished. The asylum is vastly overcrowded and money, as always, is tight.

The asylum is built of grey, local brick with stone facings. It is a fine-looking set of buildings. In the centre is the three-storey administrative block which is where my quarters are, and those of Dr Rogers and his sister. There are two wards for the men and two wards for the women – as usual, more female patients than male – and the Attendants have their own rooms.

There is little talk of treatment. Patients ARE discharged from time to time, but too often men and women stay here until they die. There is so much I want to do here. I am determined to improve the lives of these poor souls. It gives me such strength to know that you love me. Do you know how much you mean to me? I would be nothing without you.

I have not had the chance to get out on my steed as yet but Miss Rogers tells me the countryside around is very pretty and there is some good birdwatching to be had in the Fulbourn Fen.

Miss Conway is calling for me – some trouble in the female ward. I must dash.

Yours in haste but ever loving

Mac

Dearest Flo

My last letter was horribly rushed. I wanted to get a letter off to you but really had no time to write properly. Or even improperly!

Thank you for your letter. My heart beat so fast when I saw it in my pigeonhole that I nearly dropped the pile of papers I was carrying.

I am glad to hear that Tom is enjoying married life. I am trying very hard not to feel envious. Envy is not such a monster as jealousy but it is a pretty futile emotion. I know our time will come, Sweetheart.

About our answering each other's letters – there is, as you say, never cause to feel guilty. I write because I want to, and if I don't it is because I am desperately busy – never because I don't care. What we do for each other, we do for ourselves.

I have been reliving those hours we spent together before I left – sitting in the grounds of the Cathedral. There is a way you have of saying, "Oh Mac, I do love you," that hugs my heart. When you say it, I have to keep talking or else I should be speechless at the enormity of what you have said. No one has ever spoken to me quite like that. It is so natural that it need not be said, and it is so necessary to say because it is entirely natural. It is not only your words but your simple sincerity – simplicity is not much of a virtue nowadays but I think it is one of the greatest. I just hope that what I say to you carries as effectively my love.

You say I must tell you everything and not spare your feelings just because you are a woman. That is so like you. The situation here is not all bad. The Attendants on the whole are caring about their patients. Those men and women patients who can work – in the grounds or in the laundry etc. – seem reasonably content. The older, incapacitated patients are tirelessly cared for. It is the lot of the violent, unpredictable patients I should like to ameliorate. I am sure there must be better ways to deal with them than restraints and the padded room.

On a lighter note, Dr Rogers has challenged me to a tennis match this afternoon. He is lending me a racquet. Miss Rogers has promised us iced lemonade.

You have included in your letter two sheets of totally blank paper. I shall have them tested for secret ink. It may be that they are covered with the imprint of your lips. That being so, I shall kiss them, and send them slowly back with my writing on them.

All my love

Mac

Sunday 6th July 1902

Darling Flo

I am writing this on your writing paper – covered with secret ink. I could not bear to use it for anything else. It would have seemed a kind of blasphemy. I am reading your last letter as I write, drinking it in sip by sip. Tell me all things. I have such passion for you that it fills my life and I think that others must see it in me. You are at my side night and morning, and the ordinary sights of my life here at Fulbourn are filled with you.

And your letter brings me you. I know the house in Hele and I can imagine you there. Give the little maid, Ellen, my regards. Does she still have my photograph? And does Mr Garrish still have the "Abominable Animal"? I am glad you have been able to get out on your bicycle even if it is cold. I still feel the cold, even after living in England for so long. I have never known such a rotten summer. I am sorry that your father is not so well, but he has a good nurse in you.

It is like you to be interested in my work. I can do nothing about the overcrowding. In fact, there are many things that it will be difficult for me to change, but I do want to provide some sort of entertainment for these people, to take them out of themselves, give them something to think about. Just simple things like the provision of some bagatelle boards and some books and newspapers. I would like to start evening classes which both the staff and the patients could attend together. As you say, I shall have to tread carefully with Dr Rogers.

I was called out this week to an old man who was being brought from Ely Workhouse to the Asylum by the Relieving Officer. The poor chap had quite evidently died in the cab before my arrival – heart disease brought on by exhaustion. He was malnourished. The diet here may be inadequate, but it is better than that in the work house.

This morning I at last had the opportunity of exploring my surroundings a little on my bicycle. I made my way into the village and then down Church Lane and out onto the Fen. In spite of the cold, I enjoyed myself. The sky was a cloudless blue. To be free of my responsibilities for an hour or two was such a relief. I shall go again as soon as I get the chance, and take my binoculars.

Smile when you get this, that I may think of how you look.

Your Mac

Fulbourn

Sunday 13th July 1902

My Darling Girl

This daisy chain was made by me, sitting on the lawn with some of our female patients on Friday. It was such an unexpectedly warm day that I decided to get Ward F outside. These are rather unpredictable, tricky patients and the Attendants were not best pleased but I pleaded and cajoled and in the end the Garden Gang brought some chairs out for us and some of us sat on the grass and some of us sat on chairs. I started to make a daisy chain and they joined in. Some of them said they hadn't done it since they were children and it obviously brought back happier times. One of them, Miss M., was a school mistress in her pre-asylum life, and she led us in songs she used to teach the children in school. We did have a happy time, though Mrs B. (who believes she is the Duchess of Norfolk) snatched poor Miss L.'s daisy chain and broke it. However, before I or one of the Attendants could intervene, the formidable ex-schoolmistress, Miss M., told Mrs B. off in no uncertain manner so that she looked quite abashed. Miss M. told her to make Miss L. another daisy chain and she meekly did it!

I daresay I shall be in trouble with Dr Rogers if our little outing is reported back to him.

Your suggestion of a piano for the women is brilliant! Thank you.

I have had a letter from Hewitt. Will you tell him, when next you see him, how much I appreciate his taking the trouble to write? He sounds very busy at the works. What a good thing it is that he is able to take the business from your father's shoulders!

I also had a letter from India, from an old school friend, telling me that he is to be married. Of course, I am pleased for him, but it gave me a bad night, thinking about you and wanting to come and pick you up in my arms and claim you for my own. In the morning I was myself again. It will happen. Our time will come. I am utterly sure of that.

In the meantime, life is precious. We must not think of our joy being restricted to the times when we are together. We must enjoy every moment of every day, knowing that we do so in each other's love. We are so lucky – we have no doubts – no uncertainty – just pure joy. If our love spills over into the times when we are apart, then other people will benefit from it.

We are not living a tragedy, you and I. We are living in a bubble of joy.

All my love

Mac

My Girl

My mind is filled with things I want to say to you. All week I think, "I must tell Flo that," but by the time Sunday and my letter writing opportunity arrives, all is forgotten. Just know that I think of you always.

Such an uproar we have had at the asylum this week! Last year, one of the female patients escaped. She was brought back again within hours but is now found to be with child. Hers is a sad story. She was admitted two years ago. She was Norwegian and no one here could speak to her or understand what she said. How lonely and frightening it must have been for her! When the baby is born, it will have to be sent to the workhouse, of course. No one knows who the father is. Let us hope that the child is never told the circumstances of its birth.

I caught one of the male Attendants today shouting at a man on Ward B because he was being slow in getting dressed. The patient was what is called "an imbecile from birth", and slow in his thinking. I had a word with the Attendant about it afterwards and he said the patient was doing it on purpose just to annoy him. The rate of pay is very poor here and it is difficult to get good staff. Although on the whole, the staff are good, some of them I have to say are very stupid and need guidance. I wish I had time to do more teaching.

I read today that the Coronation is due to take place now on 9th August. I hope that means the Prince of Wales has recovered fully. I intend to galvanise the patients in the Sewing Room into making some bunting and celebrate the event properly here. Have they heard the news in sleepy Devon?

There is no place in my life devoid of you and you are ever held in my love.

Mac

Fulbourn

Sunday 27th July 1902

Darling Flo

The summer seems to have arrived. It is WARM at last! My window looks out onto the front lawn where two members of the Garden Gang are busy cutting the grass. They are allowed to use grass hooks which you might find surprising but they never hurt themselves and are very skilful with them. I can see the swifts charging across the sky, and swooping round the buildings, crying out with excitement. They are here such a short time.

Thank you for the photograph of your finished relief carving. It is a very lifelike owl. You have become accomplished at carving, and photography too. As a matter of fact, I think you could do anything you set your mind to do. Do you envy Mabel a little her independent life? Perhaps, but you look after the Moor House, and care for your parents without any sign of bitterness. You are a dear.

The female patients on Ward F (the daisy chain brigade) were very interested in the arrival of the piano on Wednesday. Miss L. who suffers greatly from melancholia and is mute, actually pushed her way to the front of the group standing round admiring the piano, sat down on the stool and started to play. I don't know what she was playing but it was very soft and sweet and suddenly Mrs B. was singing the words – something like, "You tell me your dream and I'll tell you mine." Two of the Attendants started to dance with each other which made the other women laugh. For a moment, it was as if we weren't in the asylum at all.

I must bend my mind to serious matters, but the heart
is with you

Mac

My Heart's Delight

I'm glad you liked the description of Ward F and the piano. The piano would not have happened if it had not been for you. Luckily, my request coincided with an imminent inspection by the subcommittee so Dr Rogers was happy to acquiesce with it.

I am beginning to feel a little more at home here. I have been invited to join the cricket team. My bowling is somewhat rusty so I have been quietly practising behind the greenhouses. That sounds dangerous but in fact I bowl with my back to the glass panes. Angus – Mr Thorne's dog – happily retrieves the balls for me. Mr Thorne is the Head Attendant here and a very good man. Like the rest of the staff, he has been at Fulbourn for many years and rather set in his ways but good hearted. He has the most tremendous singing voice and I hope to get up a little concert at Christmas. Will you come, dear heart? Oh, how happy that would make me!

You did make me smile with your account of Rose and yourself riding to the Liberal meeting on your cycles through heavy rain and then sitting through the meeting with water dripping from your hats, making puddles on the floor. Anyone else would have turned back but not you and your cousin. My adventurous girl! I feel that I take part in your experiences, just as you do in mine, and that because of this doubling up we live lives by a kind of compound interest.

I hope you forwent your habit of having a cold bath and had a good hot bath when you arrived back home. How happily I should have enveloped you in a big towel afterwards, my darling.

I have been reading, "Premiere soiree", by Rimbaud. It is not good for me. If you ever find it and read it, you will never speak to me again!

Your Mac

My Darling Flo

I opened your letter at the breakfast table this morning and nearly dropped it.

"Bad news?" asked Dr Rogers, sympathetically.

"No, quite the reverse!" said I.

Oh Florrie, are you sure it is not too far for you to travel? I know you will both be able to stay with your cousin in Westminster the night before, but it is such a long way to travel from Hereford! I feel I should tell you not to come but that is too much to ask of me. How wonderful it will be to watch the Coronation procession with you!

Yes, of course I can get a day's leave and come to London. I will tell Dr Rogers that it is an emergency, and so it is. I will have to get back here for the celebration Coronation tea which will mean our watching the procession on its way to the Abbey and leaving shortly afterwards.

I hope the Prince of Wales will be well enough to undertake the Coronation service. It is such a short time since his illness, and that illness so serious. How happy his people will be to see him. But not as happy as I shall be to see you.

I can write no more. My heart is too full. I want to dance on the rooftops of the asylum buildings.

All my love

Mac

My Darling Adventurous Flo

I have not been able to get any of my ideas sorted out since I was with you – just a few hours ago. I do not think that I shall ever catch up on all the emotions that stirred me. I have known no time in my life when I was so utterly carefree. The 9th August will now always be for me a special day, joining the 6th February as a page marker in the book that is my life. The whole day was so natural. You and I cohere and respond in a most extraordinary way. There is no one else in the world with whom I can be so completely open.

Somehow, I want to do justice to the day; tell you how wonderful you are, how much you mean to me, how every move and moment is caught up in the rhythm of my life. I fear that you will simply have to know in your dear understanding heart what I feel.

I shall never forget how excited I was, waiting on the platform for you to arrive. I must have asked a dozen times what time the train from Westminster was due to arrive. And then it was late! I was tearing my hair out, love. I was about to check my pulse to see whether a heart attack was imminent, when your train pulled in and you jumped down, a loveliness all in green – such a fetching hat, Flo, darling! And Mabel behind you, waving her umbrella and narrowly missing that poor chap behind her. I think she was a little concerned that she would be the "odd one out" and we would talk away and forget about her, but I hope we made her feel that she was welcome. I was very proud of my two beautiful girls, one on either arm.

If it hadn't been for Mabel, I don't think we would have taken the motor omnibus, would we? She was determined to try it. Quite an experience! I wonder if my friend, Sydney Rowland, has ridden in it yet. He is a keen supporter of all things mechanic. I don't think I have told you about him. I will, but just now I want to remember our day together.

There were thousands of people lining the Mall and we were lucky to secure a good viewing place. It was my first experience of a Royal procession and I was impressed by the feeling of goodwill amongst the crowd. Bank managers and bakers happily conversing together!

There was that sudden hush when we all became aware of the sound of horses trotting and the Indian cavalry came into view – I had a lump in my throat as I watched them. Dark, turbaned warriors, riding perfectly as if one with their horses – the horses delicately raising and placing their feet. It seemed as if they were marching in time to the music. A vast array of races and of castes – Tamils and Telugus, Mahrattas, Gurkhas, Sikhs and Pathans. Following them, the horse guards with their plumes and gleaming cuirasses. And then after a long line of troops, do you remember the tremendous cheer that was taken up further back by people who couldn't possibly see what was going on? The great gilded carriage with the Prince of Wales and Princess Alexandra, the Prince looking a little pale from his recent illness. I raised my hat, and you and Mabel waved your handkerchiefs. I shall never forget that moment. You were at my side where I long for you to be always.

Afterwards in St James Park – dear Mabel, such a brick! – wandering tactfully away to feed the ducks to give us time together – we sat under that friendly tree and kissed as if we were footman and maid, not the respectable people that we ought to be. I feel your lips still, your hand in my hair. You gazed steadily into my eyes as if you were learning me by heart and then you said, "You look tired, sweetheart." Dear Flo! You take care of everybody. I still can't quite believe that you are mine.

I don't know whether it was worse or better that my train went before yours. I feel still as if half of me has been pulled away. I was so glad to get your letter saying you had travelled safely home to Hereford from Westminster the next day. You are my intrepid girl. I want you to be yourself and have adventures but I also want to protect you.

So much love

Mac

Mein Liebling

I have been attempting to read a fascinating book by a man called Sigmund Freud. It is a challenge for my poor German and I cannot decipher it all but in general what he is saying is that dreams are the key to the mind.

In the early hours of yesterday morning, I was summoned to Ward B where a patient was having what appeared to be a horrific nightmare, screaming out and disturbing the other men on the Ward. By the time I arrived, the Attendant on duty had wakened the patient who was still in a highly distressed state and incontinent. The Attendant was hoping that I would give the man some chloral hydrate to calm him down.

I told the Attendant to make him more comfortable with a change of night attire and bedding. He said that in these cases they generally waited until morning. I asked him how he would feel – waking up in urine sodden sheets– and he unwillingly did as I asked.

Once back in bed, the patient started to calm down. I asked him what his dream had been about but he started to become agitated again, upon which I desisted and stayed with him until he fell asleep.

Next morning, I looked at his admission papers and found that the cause of his illness was entered as "trauma". I mentioned the matter to Dr Rogers at our morning meeting. I suggested I try talking with the patient about this "trauma" in the hope that it might have some beneficial effect, but he strictly forbade me to do so. He felt that the recalling of earlier difficulties would only agitate the man, and that good food, a calm environment and regular employment were the most effective ways of treating such a patient. My own view is that the patient has been at the asylum for over a year with no sign of improvement and perhaps it is time to try another tack. I am under orders from Dr Rogers, however, and cannot disobey him. When I am Medical Superintendent in my own asylum, I am determined to put new ideas into practice.

My darling, I'm sorry – I have run on about my own affairs – but I always want to tell you my thoughts, my ideas, my hopes. And now Miss Conway is at the door, wanting me to attend to something and I must stop.

Believe me, always,

Your Mac

My Sweet Flo

You asked what my daily duties are here at Fulbourn. They are twice as many as I have time for! I have to do two ward rounds a day – one after breakfast and one after lunch. I see any sick patients in the infirmary, both in the day time and last thing at night, dispense medicines, see the kitchens about special diets, check that the Attendants and servants are doing their duties properly, keep the patients amused and, as an afterthought, promote their mental improvement. It is this latter into which I should like to put my most strenuous efforts but sadly this is difficult to achieve.

Dr Rogers tells me that Fulbourn is like a family and he and I parents to these unfortunate souls. That is all very well, but the patients have their own families and homes, and no matter how hard their lives outside the asylum might be, I feel that that is where they belong. It is our duty to enable them to return to their loved ones as quickly as possible.

The other day I slipped into Ward B quietly to watch a new member of staff, a young local chap in his twenties called Richmond. Most of the patients had gone out to the airing courts for their exercise. One or two whose behaviour was too unpredictable to allow them to leave the ward, were lying listlessly on their beds.

Richmond was in the act of tidying the beds when I saw him stop, stand and watch one of these men, "Morgan", a giant of a man, who lay, watching the ceiling, motionless apart from his fingers which were drumming against the side of the bed.

Richmond walked over, sat down on the bed beside Morgan's and started talking quietly to him. Gradually, the fingers stilled. Richmond got up and was about to go on with his work when he suddenly realised I was there. I asked him what he had said to Morgan. He said it was only something about the weather. He had noticed that when Morgan started this finger drumming, it was a sign that he was becoming agitated, and if you could distract him, it would prevent a violent episode and there would be no need for Morgan to be restrained. This is the quality of staff we need here.

My darling, you must not encourage me to write to you about my work. I will become so tedious that you will be forced to give me up.

Darling girl, you are my love at all times.

Mac

Darling Girl

I keep your last letter in my breast pocket and whenever I feel sad or despondent, I take it out and read your words, "Mac, I shall never, ever give you up." My sweet, beloved Flo. No man ever had a woman like you. I am touched by your unfailing trust and support. I don't need – and should not need – you to say that you are "so proud of me" but to know that you are, spurs me on to do my best.

Thank you for *The Hound of the Baskervilles*. Only you would remember how disappointed I was when Conan Doyle disposed of poor Holmes over the Reichenbach Falls! And here is another full-length novel about him. Hurrah! I shall put it in my pocket the next time I am given leave to go birdwatching on Fulbourn Fen.

All my love

Mac

Dearest Girl

I read again your letter, and always with a surge of pleasure. It makes me happy when you say you are enjoying life. You have such a capacity for enjoyment.

The Chaplain was bewailing the fact yesterday that since Blackman was discharged he has no one to play the organ for his services on a Sunday. I suddenly thought me of Miss L. After the afternoon service, I kept her behind after the others had gone to their supper, ostensibly to help put hymn books away. While she was doing this, I started playing about on the organ. She came over to see what I was doing. I started to play a hymn tune (badly – my piano skills are not as advanced as yours, dear girl!), stopped mid-tune and then got up and moved away, pretending not to notice when she slipped into my place and took up where I had left off. The extraordinary thing was that she actually started to sing the words – I have never heard her utter a syllable before! I am going to have a word with the Chaplain about her playing the organ next Sunday. Strike while the iron is hot!

I have had a letter from my friend, Sydney Rowland. We knew each other when I was at Stoke under Ham. He was at Cambridge University when I met him first. He came home for the holidays to stay with his family at the Vicarage. His father is the Revd Rowland who was very good to me – I shall never forget the kind speech he gave at my leaving party – but with his sons, the Revd Rowland is strict, and I think there is little understanding between Sydney and himself. He is a man of culture, interested in art, while Sydney is a scientist with an enthusiasm for anything mechanical.

Sydney and I became friends through our mutual interest in photography. Do you remember that photograph of me taken up in the quarries on Ham Hill? That was one of Sydney's photographs.

He is going to motor up from Elstree next Saturday and spend a little time with me, a little time being all I generally have. It will be good to see the lad. You would like him. He's a practical being and good fun. Children love him.

Storms are forecast this week. Look out for lightning. I cannot manage without you.

All my love

Mac

Sunday 21st September 1902

Darling Flo

I wish you could have been with us yesterday. What fun we should all have had together! I think you would find Rowland a very amiable person.

Dr Rogers kindly allowed me a half day's leave, so after luncheon I positioned myself on the bench on the front lawn and awaited Rowland's arrival. I heard him before I saw him. There was a loud parping noise and his motor vehicle came purring round the bend in the drive and pulled up outside the front door. In an instant he had spotted me and leapt out, waving his hat wildly and shouting, "Mac!"

The dear boy! I hadn't seen him for years, and when I knew him at Stoke under Ham, he was a bright young chap, but uncertain as to his future career. He seems to have found his niche now. After qualifying, he spent two years practising as an x-ray specialist – I told you, didn't I, that he loves anything technical or mechanical? He was only 24 when he founded the Archives of Clinical Skiagraphy. But the clinical side of things didn't appeal to him. He wasn't the sort of person to have the patience to sit around waiting for patients to arrive.

Luckily, he discovered the Lister Institute. Or rather, they discovered him. It was only set up in 1891 so everything was new and exciting. He joined four years ago and worked at the laboratories in Chelsea to begin with but now his department has moved to Queensberry Lodge in Elstree. He loves the work – he is one of a team of bacteriologists working on an antitoxin for an anti-smallpox vaccine – and I think for the first time in his life feels that he is living among "family".

It was a fine afternoon so we drove in Rowland's motor car to Fulbourn Fen and sat in a hide with our binoculars. There was another chap there – a very knowledgeable man called Evans. He and Rowland had a heated discussion about whether we had seen a Montagu's Harrier or a Hen Harrier. Whichever it was, it was a rare pleasure to watch.

Rowland told me that his brother-in-law, Philip Gibbs, was at the Coronation. He was actually allowed inside the Abbey, being a journalist. He said the old black bearded Duke of Norfolk had difficulty untying the King's shoulder knots and took out a clasp knife which flashed about the King's throat while he cut them.

Rowland is staying tonight with a chap called Hayles in Cambridge – he has asked Rowland's advice about buying some x-ray equipment for Addenbrooke Hospital. Little did I know when I encouraged young Rowland's interest in photography in Stoke under Ham, that he would one day be consulted in such matters.

What a long epistle! My hand aches, but not as much as my heart aches to hold you, my Flo.

All my love

Mac

Sunday 28th September 1902

Darling Girl

It is just over a month since we met. I take the jewels of memory out and polish them over and over to keep them shiny new. I ought to be satisfied but I am not. I want more and more of you.

Your letter was a delight. Thank you for all the pictures seen through your dear eyes – the light on the water where your cousin, Edward, was fishing, the wind in the grasses, the Little Owl. Never stop writing to me about how you see life.

I talked with Rowland about my hope to some day have a laboratory here at Fulbourn and he was enthusiastic about it, saying of course we should have one. Do you remember my going to Edinburgh a few years ago, to study the pathology of insanity with Dr Ford Robertson? I was talking to several of the doctors there who had laboratories attached to their asylums. They used them not just for testing during epidemics like typhoid, but also in doing scientific research to establish the causes of lunacy. Dr Rogers humours me in granting my smaller requests but when I ask for any major change, he always says, "Ah, the Committee will never sanction that, I'm afraid," and I know very well that he never even approaches the Committee on the matter. I am determined to have one built here, however, even if I have to get the patients to build it. If only we could have as modern a laboratory as your dear father has in his cider factory.

Miss L. played the organ for us beautifully in chapel this morning. The Chaplain was delighted. Even Dr Rogers commented upon it at luncheon.

This afternoon I cycled down to the Fen with "The Hound of the Baskervilles" in my pocket. The day was misty and grey with no sign of the sun. I spread a rug and commenced to read. After an hour or so I was so engrossed in the tale that I could almost imagine I was sitting out on the moor. A dog howled in the distance and, I promise you, your practical, hard-headed doctor nearly jumped out of his skin! I decided to cycle back to Fulbourn and continue reading in the comparative comfort and safety of my little room!

So much love

Mac

Darling Flo

Mr Thorne's boy, Cecil, came to see me last week to say he and some of the other lads wanted to get up an impromptu cricket match on the lawn this afternoon. Would this be allowed and would I be umpire? Of course I said yes. You must know that we are very much a family affair here. People come to work at Fulbourn; they marry other members of staff and eventually their children grow up and join the staff too.

Dr Rogers is away for a month and not back until the 11th and I am in charge, so I arranged for as many of the patients as possible to come out onto the lawn to watch the match with the Attendants and nurses, and everyone had a very enjoyable time. Miss Duke did us proud with a wonderful tea. It was late in the year for cricket but the weather has been dry and warm and I think the lawn took no harm.

Do you remember that young Attendant about whom I wrote to you, Charles Richmond? It was he who distracted the patient, Morgan, on Ward B, when he might have developed a violent episode. He was near me in the tea tent and I started to draw him out regarding his ideas on nursing mental patients. I could see several of the Attendants and nurses nearby listening carefully, some looking scornful (after all, young Richmond has not been with us very long) but others looking interested. I intend to get some formal teaching for the staff underway as soon as I can.

We are in desperate need of another Assistant Medical Officer. Most asylums of our size have at least two. I must say, I would welcome another doctor to discuss cases and plan the way forward. Rowland's visit has made me realise how lonely my position is. If you and I were married, we would be living snugly in a little house in the village. Should you like a large family, Flo? I know I should. Time is against us, but Dr Rogers is close to retirement age, and with you by my side, I am confident that I could step into his shoes.

To sleep now, to meet you in my dreams.

Love

Mac

Darling Florence

I know you don't like being called "Florence" but it is a beautiful name and sometimes you must allow me to use it.

I was called out to see an Indian patient in the night. He is blind and elderly – nobody knows how old – not even he knows. It is unknown either why he was initially admitted. He was transferred to Fulbourn many years ago from a workhouse. I remember the first time I saw him, sitting in the day room, staring at the wall with those sightless eyes. I spoke to him in his native language and his face lit up.

It has been borne in on me that it is not death that is the problem but rather old age. I should gladly skip the one to fall into the arms of the other. Sometimes in the wee hours, I try to imagine what my life would be like if I had not met you. Life is so uncertain. Suppose I had not met you – I could have fallen ill and lost my position – who would have cared? My family could not have helped, being so far away and with the trouble the indigo business is in. I could have ended up like the blind old Indian, in the workhouse. Knowing that there is one person who cares makes such a difference.

I remember when I was training to become a doctor, receiving the news that my brother, Julian, had died. Not only was my heart wrung with grief at his loss, but my means of support was gone. I had to postpone my exams. I had to work as a Medical Assistant to raise the money to continue my studies. I became ill with overwork. Those were dark days. Then I found the position with Dr Walter at Stoke under Ham, and he and the other villagers were so very kind to me. One needs love in order to keep well.

This is a gloomy letter. I'm sorry. Not only is it the anniversary of my brother's death seven years ago, but I have had news from my brother George to say that two of his children have died on the same day in Allahabad. They were but five and three years old. The wee mites had hardly arrived in this world.

One good piece of news– the Committee have agreed to consider appointing an Assistant Medical Officer. Thank God!

All my love

Mac

Sunday 19th October 1902

My Dear Girl

I'm sorry about my last letter. Your reply simultaneously cheered me up and made me feel ashamed of myself.

Dr Rogers has asked me to arrange some entertainment for Christmas and I have written off for the script of a play by Joseph Lunn. "Family Jars" – do you know it? Annie Rogers saw it produced in Cambridge some years ago and said it was very amusing. Do you remember when you came to see *Babes in the Wood* at Burghill? Being aware of you in the audience, I nearly forgot my lines. But it was marvellous to have you there.

This afternoon I cycled to the Fen. Autumn is late this year. I stopped for a few minutes under a huge ancient oak tree on the village green. The leaves are only now beginning to be golden, so that looking up one sees a delicious pattern of green and gold against a blue, blue sky. It is so easy to think of you. You are conjured up by the wind in my hair, the waft of woodsmoke, the sound of a robin. You are a part of me.

This is a nothing, but the most loving nothing that has ever been written.

Your own Mac

PS How is your toothache? A hare's foot worn around the neck is a cure for toothache. Would I were a hare's foot!

My Own Dear Intended

Such an anxious letter from you! Of course I understand why you do not wish our engagement to be made public. I know it is not just "worrying what people would say". Our love for each other is precious – it is hard to expose it to the disapproval of those who do not understand. You say you could not bear to hear me traduced. I could not bear the thought of your being the butt of cruel comments and I not there to comfort you. The thought pierces me to the heart.

When Rowland was here, we went for a walk in the grounds after supper. I asked him whether he had a young lady. He told me he was much too busy with his work to think about girls. He supposed I was a confirmed bachelor. I said I was no such thing, that I was betrothed to a beautiful, intelligent girl whom I could not wait to marry. I think he was quite taken aback! I showed him your photograph and he said you had a sweet face. If only that sweet face were before me now! I should gently frame it with my hands and kiss it.

You cannot know how my body and mind respond to you. You are of that substance and life that sets a man's soul on fire.

I love you.

Mac

My Darling Flo

We had our first read through of *Family Jars* this afternoon. A surprising number of people attended and all were enthusiastic. A farce is always good fun to put on. Miss Annie said this would be the first Christmas entertainment at Fulbourn for some years. I play "Porcelain", a China merchant.

There will be a concert beforehand with Mr Thorne conducting. Did I tell you that Mr Thorne's first name is Mendelssohn? He is a fine bass singer with a flowing moustache and a substantial paunch. Very impressive looking. It was he who showed me round when I first arrived. It seems such a long time ago now.

We have set the date for 23rd December and plan to put it on in the Central Hall. I am determined that a general invitation will go out to people in Fulbourn village. I feel it is important that they know what we do up here at the asylum.

I was looking up a patient's record in the office the other day when I came across a report about Fulbourn Asylum at the time Dr Lawrence was Superintendent here back in 1862.

It stated that no restraints were used on the patients, the windows had no bars and the doors no bolts. It looked like a hospital and not like a prison as it does now. The way that this was done was by constant watching of the patients to make sure they did not come to any harm. And this was 40 years ago! We have gone backward in our care of the mentally ill, not forward. Of course, with the numbers in our asylums now, it would not be possible to have that system in place, but oh! if only we could! I should like to be wealthy enough to set up my own asylum along those lines.

Goodnight, love

Your Head in the Clouds Mac

Darling Girl

Yesterday, I was given permission to go into Cambridge and discovered this little book in Macmillan and Bowes, *The Tale of Peter Rabbit*, which I thought you might like to send to young Will and Pick in Australia for Christmas. Is it too late to get there in time? Pick is too young to read it but he might like to look at the pictures. I think the illustrations very fine.

I'm afraid you must miss your sister, Ivy, very much.

I counted eight male blackbirds on the lawn this morning. Very bright in the bills. Where are all the females?

I have been reading a book Dr Rogers lent me about the Spartans – how their enemies were dropped into a deep cave from which there was no escape. And I wondered whether, if I were in a situation of no hope, the thought and image of you would strengthen my nerve. I knew that it would. How awful to have nothing, to know that there was no love, no care for you in the world.

There are so many lonely, loveless people. Yet <u>you</u> make friends wherever you go, and they are not just friends – I know how greatly you are loved and respected.

All love, my dear girl

Mac

My Heart's Desire

We had a rehearsal for *Family Jars* this afternoon. Mr Fox plays my son, while Mr Arthur Case is my faithful Foreman. Mr John Merry (one of the Attendants) is playing "Joe, the office boy" which will be amusing as in fact he is in his forties and has a large family himself. Both Mr Fox and Mr Merry are also singing in the concert beforehand. I remember when we put on a similar entertainment at Burghill, being surprised at how much talent there was hidden amongst the staff.

None of these names will mean anything to you. If we were married, you would know the people I work with and they would know you. One day...

Dr Rogers complimented Miss L. on her rendition of "Onward Christian Soldiers" at the organ this morning and she smiled. I have never seen her smile before.

At luncheon, I brought up the subject of doing away with locks on some of the ward doors but I'm afraid the idea met with strong opposition from Dr Rogers. There are patients here who have no desire to "escape" into the outside world and, indeed, live in fear of being released. Surely there is no need for locked doors in such cases? The Medical Superintendent, however, is ultimately held responsible for any absconsions and so policy is led by anxiety.

The snow is coming down fast outside my window. Here in my little room I have a fire and all is cosy. The firelight flickers over the bookcase and pauses lovingly for a second over *The Hound of the Baskervilles*.

Yesterday, I discovered an old newspaper lining one of my drawers. I was instantly drawn to an article about Egremont Folly. Do you remember our visiting it when I came to stay with you in Devon? It was a fascinating place with marble chimney pots and amber door handles, and bell pulls made of ivory. The newspaper article stated that the valuable portions had been sold off and the whole place blown up last November. How sad, that one of the places we went to together has been destroyed! The chap who was conducting the blowing up operation tripped and fell and narrowly escaped being crushed by a heavy pillar. Let that be a lesson to him! I'm joking darling.

You make me happy and that makes me wordless, except to say

I love you

Mac

Darling Girl

"Kiss me anywhere you please", you write rashly in your letter. That is an invitation to a rather protracted experience. I wonder why I find kissing you so very special. Because it is a chance that I have only rarely? Because I have never kissed anyone with such intensity or been kissed so in return? Yes, both of these. But it is because we hold out to each the soul. We search out our inward parts and dreams and find them so familiar and comforting. It is an expression of something deep, but it is also just pure naked pleasure in the touch of you.

You talk about your letter being intense. That is all that matters. Never with a "smothering" intensity but with that absolute certainty that says: "Go and do all that you need to do, and know that I shall be here when you come back." How many marriages would be better for that philosophy? I wrote to you that I wanted to see you. "We have a little more living to do," you said. How I love you. How I love your steadiness.

I am reading your letter through again – steadily, comfortably. Watching your face. Is your nose screwed up as you think of what to write? I don't think so. You write with a gush. You set out your feelings without straining them through a mesh of worry. You say how awful it would be – the very worst – if I believed that you were not telling me the truth. Now who is being foolish? "Dinna fash yersel'", as my dear father used to say. You and I are incapable of telling each other an un-truth.

I have been reliving that blessed 9th August when we were together. The picture in my mind for ever is of your serious eyes looking right into me, searching me out and trusting my love. So fearlessly they look and there is a contentment in the seriousness.

I love you. And I love life because I love you.

Your Mac

30th November 1902

My Darling

Dr Rogers is away for two weeks. There is a great deal of extra work but I have to admit to a feeling of holiday, with everything rather more relaxed than usual.

When he was away in September, one of the Attendants went absent without leave, returned blotto and gave the Charge Attendant a black eye. I wonder if anything as exciting will happen this time. Anything which interrupts institutional life is rather welcomed than otherwise.

Mr Thorne was reporting to me in a convoluted fashion an incident which had occurred on one of the Men's Wards. Mr Thorne never uses one word where two will do. I remembered the word "perrisological" from your last letter – as mentioned by the vicar – and I said, "Mr Thorne, I do wish you would not be quite so perrisological." That silenced him!

Please do thank your father for his very helpful letter full of advice about my laboratory. I will be writing to him myself but would be grateful if you could pass on my thanks. It was kind of him to take the trouble, especially as I know he is not well.

Darling, how I should like to see you in your new blue dress!

Wrap it gently into tissue, lay it in a special drawer So that I who this day miss you May know you as you were before.

Have I told you of late that I love you? I do.

Your Mac

Darling Girl

Are you glad to be back at Moor House for Christmas? You will be caught up now in a whirl of seasonal events. By Christmas I expect you will have quite forgotten my name. If that is the case, I shall have to come to Hereford and remind you.

Only two weeks until the Christmas entertainment. Last week I was in despair and could not imagine our being ready in time. Arthur Case (my faithful foreman, Delph) had only managed two rehearsals, and Miss Gumbley, who plays my daughter-in-law, was continually "ad libbing" so that I was never quite sure when to speak or what I was replying to. However, either the imminence of the Entertainment evening or my threatening to abandon the whole thing, seems now to have galvanised the cast.

Our carpenter, Mr Bell, has made a superb job of the scenery. At least, when we all forget our words, the audience will be able to sit back and admire that.

I have been on tenterhooks lest I should not be able to get to Cambridge to collect your Christmas present but I was given leave of absence to go yesterday and I have it safe, ready to post to you. I hope you like it.

The presents you are making for your family sound delightful. If you were ever to be shipwrecked, you would very soon make your desert island decorative and cosy. What fun it would be to be marooned on a desert island together! You would soon make our little palm tree cabin homely while I went off to find fish and coconuts. Knowing you, of course, you would want to climb the coconut trees and throw the fruit down to me. They would inevitably land on my head. My delicious reverie seems to have ground to a halt.

Darling, perhaps you had better find a lover who has more sense, not to mention more money. Ah me!

No lover could ever have more love for you, however, sweetheart

Your Mac

My Dearest Flo

I am so very sorry to hear that your father is unwell again. You must not, of course, leave him. I had not dared to let myself hope that you would be able to come here for the entertainment on the 23ʳᵈ and so my disappointment is not as keen as it might have been had I been actively anticipating your arrival. The thought of my coming to Hereford in the New Year sustains me. If Dr Rogers permits.

The dress rehearsal is next Sunday. I see my fellow actors while on my rounds and we quote our lines to each other, much to the bewilderment of the other members of staff.

No, I am not going to give you the veriest whiff of a clue as to what your Christmas present from me is. I don't care if you are dying of curiosity – you will just have to thole it, to quote Mr McCutchan Senior.

I wish I could watch you open it, but I know your dear face so well that I can picture you sitting with your family, opening your presents and saving mine, perhaps, for last, when everyone will be so caught up with looking at their own presents that they will not notice the little box. There! You have made me give away the fact that it is small! I shall finish this letter before any other clues escape.

I love you, girl

Mac

21st December 1902

Darling Naughty Flo

You are a BAD girl! When I told you – months ago – to go and see the new Bee Meter at the Meter Works, it was for your own interest. I didn't mean that you should buy me one! You are much too extravagant. It arrived yesterday. I was very strongminded and waited until today to open it, as you had written NOT TO BE OPENED BEFORE 21ST DECEMBER very firmly on the outside. Apart from yourself, it was the nicest birthday present I could have had. Thank you. I am going to have a tremendous amount of fun with it, and I am sure my photographs will now be perfect.

I have been boasting to Rowland about your father's friendship with Alfred Watkins, telling him how AW would come round to the house and talk about his photographic meter invention and how your father encouraged him to take out the patent. The best inventions are always the simple ones, where you wonder why no one has thought of them before.

I am on tenterhooks about Dr Rogers approving my leave in the New Year. I want to use my Bee Meter <u>with you</u>, my darling.

You will be pleased to hear that the dress rehearsal today was utterly disastrous. This means, of course, that the actual performance will be perfect. I send you a copy of the programme.

I love you, now and always

In haste

Your Mac

My Flo

> 'We'll gently walk, and sweetly talk,
> While the silent moon shines clearly;
> I'll clasp thy waist and fondly prest,
> Swear how I lo'e thee dearly.'

Thank you, Darling, for the beautiful little edition of Burns' love poems. I couldn't have asked for a nicer present. Except that, of course, there was an even nicer one inside, resting upon the title page.

My heart beat fast when I saw it – a curl of your lovely hair. You will grow older, and I will love you just the same, but this little lock will always be as it is today. You cannot imagine how privileged, how honoured I am to have something which is your very self.

To say "thank you" is not enough. Oh, if you were here!

Mac

My Darling

As the year draws to a close, I think of the happiness that you have given me. I always want to clutch the last days and wring them out. You are special. I wonder if you ever get tired of my saying it. I read that women do weary of hangers-on. Steadiness is one thing, but excitement is another. I want to give you both.

This is the last letter I shall write to you in 1902. This time last year, I was at Burghill and you were much closer to me in terms of miles, but in terms of attainability, you were further away. By Christmas 1903, who knows?

I am so glad you liked the silver locket. You may put inside it the image of whomever you please, but know, when it rests upon your breast, that it has been kissed by one who loves you.

Family Jars was such fun! The difficulty was that when I was desperately going over my lines in a quiet place behind the stage before the entertainment started, there would always be someone finding me out, wanting me to do something. It mattered not a jot when I forgot my lines, however, as the audience laughed all the more.

Mr Miller has done us proud with a huge Christmas tree in every day room, and the staff have been helping the patients to make Christmas decorations so that the place looks almost cheery. Even the back wards look somewhat improved with the addition of holly and paper chains. Christmas is a bitter sweet time for our patients. I saw many of them looking tearful during the carol service as the familiar music brought back memories of home and happier times. My resolution for 1903 is to make the year as happy for them as I possibly can.

My other resolution – one which I have had ever since I met you – is to work and work and work until I can make myself worthy of you and make you mine.

I wish you and your family the very happiest of years. Give your parents my very best regards. I want you to go among all whom you meet wearing the perfume of our happiness.

Love – always

Mac

Do you realise, Flo Darling, that we have known each other now for six years! I opened a book the other day and found an old letter of yours where you wrote "Christmas seems extra special this year. It is the first year with you in it… I think this year has been the happiest of my life." It is my wish to make you go on being happy. I positively insist. Perhaps one day we will sit by the fire – the children abed – and we shall reread our old letters and laugh – "did I really write that?" And we shall groan at our sillinesses, but we shall know that nothing was silly – but all wonderful. Our children's children will read one day and be delighted that we could have such passions.

My love for you is beyond the years, and beyond the stars

Mac

Sunday 11th January 1903

My Dear Glorious Girl

You write in your letter that you are happy. That makes my day sing. At the end of the day it is that that I wish to know. I want to see you, but I can cope.

I have two pieces of news for you. One bad and one good.

The first is that the Visitors have refused my request to build a laboratory at Fulbourn. They say the funds are not available. Well, I know what you will say – never give up! So, I am going to spend the next few months designing my laboratory and then in the spring I shall choose some of the more able patients to build it. It may take years but I am determined to have my laboratory. I should like to achieve something to be remembered here at Fulbourn. Shut the door against me until I have done something half glorious, darling, and then take me in your arms.

The good news – the best of news – is that Dr Rogers has approved my leave – hooray! It is – weather permitting – for the end of January. Now pray don't tell me that you are going to Devon or to Malvern!

I could stay for a week if your parents can bear it. Tell me quickly if it is possible. Do you realise it is five months since we last saw each other in London? You will think I look dreadfully old, I daresay. You won't recognise me at Hereford Station. I shall have to wear a label, "Dr Mac – handle with care – to be collected by Flo." I shall be on tenterhooks until you confirm.

Ever

Your Aged Mac

Darling Girl

Your letter made me very happy. Tell your parents how grateful I am for their generosity. You say any day, any time. I should like to come on Saturday 31st January. I shall look up the trains and let you know the time of my arrival. The weather seems benign at present. Let us hope the snow holds off until I am safely in Moor House and then it can snow and snow and snow.

Whatever happens, I want you to know that you have given me a happiness beyond anything I could dream. My sky lights up with the Northern Lights (which I have always wanted to see) and my desert bursts into oasis flower.

I find it so strange that you share my interests, and are often there before me, thinking and finding out. There is a consanguinity of soul and purpose. We are perfectly aligned and compatible. I suppose lovers have always said that, but most will not have known each other as we do. Most imagine how the other is, and dream of how they would want them. But we "know" because we write our inner thoughts, because we can survive only on honesty. Living at a distance, everything would wither if we did not intrigue each other with our real selves. You do know me better than anyone because you listen to my longings and my fears.

Would you like me to bring anything? A pheasant, a cheese, a jewel from some Eastern temple?

Your own

Mac

Sunday 25th January 1903

My Darling Flo

Six days until I see you. Every morning I jump out of bed and rush to the window to check the weather, and every morning the roofs of the asylum are dripping with rain and I rub my hands gleefully. Not a sign of snow to keep me from journeying towards you.

I had to report to the coroner this week. A man was brought to the asylum from Ely after having several epileptic fits, and died the day after he arrived. The coroner gave a verdict of "death from exhaustion from acute mania, post-epileptic, accelerated by injuries received during a fit prior to his admission to the asylum." When I carried out a post-mortem, his bones were exceedingly brittle, possibly due to malnutrition, poor man. I was glad that the asylum was cleared of responsibility. He was treated gently here, as was stated in the coroner's report. People outside of the asylum are always quick to assume the worst – there is such a horror of the place in the hearts of the common people.

I shall bring my papers showing the design of my new laboratory-to-be. Perhaps your father would look over them for me and give me his opinion if he is feeling well enough. I don't wish to worry him. I was feeling a little seedy a few days ago and the thought struck me that I should not come and put your father in danger of infection but thank heaven it has passed and I am fighting fit again.

Dr Rogers is quite impossible. He is a charming man but has no enthusiasm other than for the development of his golf swing or his tennis back hand. When I remember Dr Morrison and his innovative ideas at Burghill! One of Dr M's ideas was to revolutionise the dress of the female patients. They looked as if they were clothed in sacks. Dear Matron took up his ideas with gusto and brought them to fruition so that at last the women patients looked like their sisters outside the asylum. You have no idea how it improved morale. Our Matron here at Fulbourn is kindly and efficient but if ever I should ask her to make a change, she would say, "Certainly, doctor. I will refer the matter to the superintendent." And that would be that!

This is the last letter I shall write to you before I take your hand in mine and say, "Flo darling!" and kiss you in front of everyone on Hereford Station.

Yours always

Mac

Darling, darling Flo

I have spent all afternoon walking, and wanting, and thinking over the moments, and seeing you so clearly, so dearly. It is your eyes that hold my heart; I watch them when they are lost in thought. Their horizons are so big and far, and yet they show me the processes of your heart. There was the time when we had the house to ourselves. Your mother was organising teas for the Primrose League meeting and your father was away on business. Such a blessed time sitting by the fire, not talking. Your head was on my shoulder, and your eyes were closed, and you looked at peace – my Madonna. I watched your face, perhaps as a mother watches her babe.

I have begun the letter in a hundred ways as I walked. "I must start by telling her <u>that</u>," I have thought. That will be the way. That will remind her of what I feel. But alas, the ideas have all gone like the big fluffy clouds that are about today, and against wide acres of blue.

I had thought of writing on one sheet of paper – quite separate – what I feel about you. Rice paper – so that you could eat it afterwards. But it is no good because I want to say it all the time. You are lovely, but if you were lovely without being you, I should not love you. If you were lovely and anyone else, I should pass you by in the street. Oh yes, I might say, "I like her hair", and watch you, but you would not stir me to distraction. But <u>you</u> do just that, and it is because you are so honest and generous with me. Men do not expect women to have desire and so they are shy of showing it, but you are too honest to dissemble. You are giving to me all the time. If there was a boundary, then

I should have to stop and inspect my thoughts to ensure that they were appropriate. But the boundaries are what <u>we</u> instinctively set, and what we want. And they coincide. I should protect you, and you me. And because that is so we have no fears. Our willingness means that there is no desperation. Desire is for what one cannot have. In your happy loveliness you give me everything.

It was the most wonderful time for me. Your family – so welcoming– so energetic! How far we walked! I hope I did no long-term damage to Tom's bicycle. It was kind of him to lend it even if he knew nothing about it.

I had a lump in my throat when you told me you were learning German and had started to read Freud's *Interpretation of Dreams*. Nobody else would do that for me. You are my marvellous girl.

Please thank your parents for me. I had such a happy time in dear Moor House. We know we may not see each other again for many months, and leaving you is a bereavement, but you make it as easy for me as you can. A firm handshake and an admonition to board the train before it leaves without me. Thank you for being entirely you.

With my love

Mac

Darling Flo

I went down to the Fen today. The trees were like a pen and ink etching – every bough distinct. I love all seasons because of you. I have been running through our week together in my mind, trying to keep the memories bright and clear.

I was glad there was time to fit in a visit to Mrs Moore. She and Henry were so kind to me when I first moved to Burghill from Stoke under Ham and knew nobody except Cuthbert Morrison. It was a shame we didn't see Henry. Poor chap, running around every lodging house in Hereford checking for smallpox. I know of no one more assiduous in their duties as Medical Officer of Health.

And Etta in her new home! I remember how worried you were last spring when she married Mr Levason – and he twice her age! But she seems content, happy to have her own household to run, and he is a good sort – very keen about his boys' industrial school. There might have been resentment on the part of his daughters but that does not appear to be the case. I remember the girl I met seven years ago, so full of life and gaiety. I could have wished to see her married for love, with her own children around her, but contentment and security is no bad thing, and as you say, there are different kinds of love. I feel sad that there will come a day when her husband will no longer be alive and she will be alone with no one to care for her. We must be there for her when that time comes.

You are all in all to me and I love you.

Mac

PS I wander around in a day dream, thinking about your father's laboratory. It is marvellous. If only mine could be half as good.

My Darling

You fill your days with friends, and new hobbies, and books. My days with their routine pass so quickly. I follow the same timetable – meals/ward rounds/sanatorium/chapel/dispensary – and there is always some emergency. It seems as if it is time for bed the moment I get up, and time to get up the moment my head reaches the pillow. This is a bad time of year for deaths in the asylum. People lose hope, get ill and slip away. When life is grim, your letters are a lifeline to happiness.

Did you read in the papers about the fire at Colney Hatch? Such a terrible tragedy! 52 lives lost, but the courage of those nursing assistants trying to get the patients out! The patients were housed in a temporary building which was not fit for purpose. Our buildings here are poorly built but at least they are permanent. I arranged a fire drill when I heard of the Colney Hatch fire. Some of the assistants grumbled but most, I think, were glad of it.

It is evening here, and I am sitting by the fire in my old leather armchair. Your last letter is on my knee. You are here; and you are not here. You know how much I want you, how much – God help me – I need you, but I want to know that you are happy to wait. I feel sometimes that I am wasting your life. Never, ever stay with me for pity or out of a sense of loyalty. Love does not work that way. It has to be all or nothing. If you should fall in love with someone else, I should truly be glad for you because your happiness is my happiness, just as I know that mine is yours.

Well, that is all very serious! Meanwhile – I love you dearly, clearly, cheerily,

Darling Girl

Mac

Darling Flo

You are a treasure beyond all my hopes and deservings. That you should write such things gives my life bright hope and a quicker step. Thank you, my darling.

On Monday I went before the Visitor's Committee to put before them my idea about the patients building the laboratory. I took your curl in my breast pocket and felt capable of anything. Your love is a most extraordinary strengthening presence, even though you are so far away. You say: "I believe in you; you have my love always." You make me know that I can do things. I don't have to believe in myself, because you believe in me and say everything will go well.

My dear girl, the Committee said yes! As a matter of fact, there has been so much argument lately about who will fund enlargements to the Asylum that I think they were glad to approve of anything which will save some money.

You say in your letter that you cried because you forgot to thank me for the little book I sent you. Never cry for me – there is no need because you make me happy. You never let me down because that would need an effort of the will. And if there was that effort of the will, then you would not mind about what I felt. Nor can you think that I shall feel let down, or lonely, or disappointed. It simply is not possible – until that moment when you tell me that things have changed. If that time comes, then you must promise to tell me. You must promise me that. Honesty is our only strength – with each other and with others. I do not believe that that moment will come, but if it did, know that you have given me myself, and that because of you, all is well with me forever.

I am glad that you are going to the South of France with your parents. It will be good for your father's health and it will be interesting for you to have a change of scene. It makes little difference to us where the other is as long as our letters arrive. Just keep safe, my girl, and beware of drinking the water.

Look out for the hoopoe. I have seen them in India but never in this country. I should like to see one again. You may well be lucky in the South of France.

My regards to your parents and tell them that I wish them a good journey.

This must be all if it is to go. It is winged with my love and sealed with my kiss.

Mac

Sunday 8th March 1903

Darling Flo

Snow and crows. Black and white. Good snow for snowballs but it is going quickly. The trees looked lovely as I walked over to the Thornes' cottage this afternoon.

Am I right in thinking that the intensity of love for those of riper years is much stronger? It ought not to be so. It should be tempered with wise reservations and controlled by reason. I do not find it like that at all, but like a fire which burns all up. A clichéd image but it is so. They say that intense emotions do not last. I have never felt our love as less than intense. Perhaps because we are so far apart and hunger cannot be satisfied. It is a consuming force. I cannot imagine a kind of dull steadiness with you. A going on and on – yes. But never a taking-for-granted rubbing along. Well, I seem to thrive on it. Love has kept all winter colds at bay, and goodness knows I have consorted enough with people who have them.

Sleety snow is now hurling against my window and the wind is thumping in my chimney. On the wall beside me is your little painting of Victoria Bridge in Hereford. We stood upon that bridge, we two, and watched the river in silence. It was the day I before I came to Fulbourn.

Darling, I am not sure if I should tell you this and raise your hopes but I cannot bear to be anything but honest with you. I have applied for a position as Medical Superintendent near Bristol. Dr Rogers has frequently been absent from the asylum since I have started work at Fulbourn, and I have therefore had sufficient experience in running an asylum to feel quite confident of my ability to fulfil the role at Bristol. Dr Rogers assures me that the

Visitors are happy to give me a good reference. I have high hopes. If I should be given the position, not only will I be living closer to you, my love, but it may be possible for us to at last be joined in marriage and start our happy life together. God willing. God willing.

Your Mac

My Darling Flo

Happy St David's Day, my love! If you were here with me now, I should pick an armful of daffodils for you. The lawn at the front of the asylum is covered with little bunches of them. There was a pair of grey wagtails foraging around the lime trees early this morning. Lovely, neat, fastidious creatures.

I hope this will arrive before you leave for Menton, and although I told you it makes no difference, I find myself strangely bereft that you will be so far away. The South of France would take me a long time to reach if you were ill. So, you must stay well and happy, and enjoy every moment of your weeks there. I so much want you to have a fun, unfettered, unbothered time. By the by, did you know that Robert Louis Stevenson stayed in Menton?

When I see your letter with the foreign post mark on the envelope, my heart will leap up and I will scurry off with it. It is always so, it does not change. It is not a sensation to which I shall ever become conditioned. It takes me anew every time.

In one of the women's wards this morning, a nurse was playing the piano – your piano. It was a tune I knew well. My father used to play it. He had only to hear a tune and he could play it. He loved music and dancing. He would tell funny stories too. I remember he and my brother, Julian, capping stories and having us all in fits of laughter. They would have loved you. I wish you could have known them. I wish you could have known my mother, too. She had a mercurial temperament. She would fly into a tremendous passion in a moment. My father, however, could always make her laugh. Her grandfather came from Nantes in France and fought with Napoleon. Her father was killed in the Mutiny. She gave birth to eleven children in all and raised nine of them. Strange how music brings back memories.

I went to the Fen with my ornithologist friend, Humble Evans today. I enjoy his company a great deal. We watched a barn owl circling slowly round and round. It was close and slightly below us. The full moon of its face and its big eyes. Every now and then it would check and dive, and come up with nothing. Then, on about the sixth attempt it was successful and we could see it pulling and plucking in the tussocks. There were harriers too – beautiful. I love the slow silhouette line of their wings as they quarter the ground. Two of them cartwheeled and twisted in mating flight. Sometimes they fly upside down to impress the other, and pass food from talon to talon. What fun we should have, my darling, if we were harriers together!

Sweet girl, you mean so much. Live your life to the full but remember that.

Mac

My Darling Flo

I sit here in my old armchair with the window open, listening to the soft September rain. The Garden Gang have been having bonfires all day and the aroma of woodsmoke drifts in. Autumn is on its way. Why is it that evening scents are so beautifully haunting? If you are sad, they increase your melancholia.

Last Sunday, I was sitting next to you in Bradninch Church. We have become so at ease with each other, so complementary that it seems horribly unnatural to be apart. I find I cannot bear the thought of your being unhappy. I would not rob you of your peace of mind for anything in the world.

When I was with you, I felt as a lover. Now, I feel protective and fatherly towards you. I think I did not take enough care of you when I was in Devon. I know you are an intrepid girl – you are always at full tilt – walking and cycling – but we walked for miles – I don't believe it stopped raining once for the entire month! – and I never asked you if you were tired or cold, or if your feet hurt, or if you were hungry or thirsty. You will laugh at me for worrying about you. We worry about each other. Our feelings for each other are the same, balanced equally on the scales. I cannot become accustomed to the idea that there is someone who cares desperately if I am unhappy or tired or ill, but you do, and I care in just the same way for you. There is a John Donne poem which goes:

"What ever dyes, was not mixt equally;
If our two loves be one, or, thou and I
Love so alike, that none doe slacken, none can die."

A love that is equal, like ours, will never die.

Give my regards to your parents and thank them for their hospitality. Theirs is always an open house to relatives and friends and poor worn out medical men. I feel at home with them because my own parents showed the same generous hospitality – a Scottish/French trait, I always thought, but perhaps it is a Devon trait also.

As for you, there is only my poor love which you turn into a glory.

I am yours

Mac

PS The motor bicycle and sidecar arrived while I was away. I enclose a photograph. I hope one day to take you for a ride in it, dear girl whom I much want to hug.

Sunday 13th September 1903

My darling adventurous Flo

I might have known you would not be content to ride in a wicker sidecar! What on earth will your family say when you buy a motor bicycle? They will think I am a bad influence. Very well – I give in! We will travel the Fulbourn lanes side by side.

But what shall I do now with my wicker sidecar? I invited Matron to come for a spin but she refused to get into it. She says she doesn't trust my driving. Such impudence!

You write that you think I am more Scottish than French. My mother would not have it so! Her grandfather served as a lieutenant in Napoleon's army before coming to India. We children were rocked in the cradle to the sound of French lullabies; as we grew up, our nurse scared us with native tales in Bengali and our father read us the poems of Burns. Is it any wonder that your Mac is a poor muddle of a man?

The patients are full of coughs and colds, and I have a putrid sore throat. I told Mr Thorne that I had been gargling with whisky and he said he thought it was a waste of good liquor.

I love you, girl. Perhaps not as much as I shall next year, but it seems like it.

Your Mac

My Darling Flo

I have to admit that I have my favourites among my patients. One of these is dear Miss L. who has made great progress recently and is due to be discharged. Her sister has come to see her every visiting day and will take her into her own home. I shall miss her.

I have asked the Committee to consider rescinding their order forbidding visitors now that the smallpox epidemic is over. Some of the patients have gone downhill considerably since not receiving visitors. We have been having to vaccinate every new admission but hopefully we can now stop doing this.

So, you are off to Malvern again with your parents for the month of October. Will you be staying in the same hotel? If different, remember to send me the address, my darling. I hope the waters are beneficial to your father's health.

I have nothing to send this time but my love, which if it travels as heavy and heartfelt as it is, will necessitate an envelope stuck all over with stamps. I like it when you say "Your Flo", and so, with love

Your Mac

1st November 1903

Darling Flo

Did I no' tell ye about the smallpox epidemic? Dinna fash yersel', girl! I am well and my throat is better. I am just rather tired.

Dr Rogers and I joined the Committee on Monday to interview the candidates for 2nd Assistant Medical Officer. There were five applicants – four gentlemen and one lady – Dr Gertrude Grogan. She arrived a few minutes late which instantly prejudiced one member of the Committee against her, but I felt at once that this was a person with whom I could work comfortably.

During the post-interview discussions, the aforesaid Committee member said he saw no necessity for employing a lady doctor. I pointed out that many asylums were now appointing lady doctors as the majority of the patients are female. I was surprised to find that I had Dr Rogers' support. The result is that she has been given the post. She is due to start at the end of November. Hoorah! I have been waiting and hoping for this for over a year now.

Mr Thorne is keen to start organising the Christmas entertainment. It seems only yesterday that we were performing *Family Jars*.

Shall you be at Moor House for Christmas? I hope so. You will be training the new dog, Bobby, to distribute the Christmas presents. How I wish I could be there, but it is of no use to repine. I shall be there in spirit.

All my love

Mac

PS I make it sound as if Dr Grogan was given the post because she was a female – she was, in fact, much the most qualified applicant.

Darling Flo

Our Christmas entertainment this year is going to be *Liberty Hall*. I play Sir Hartley Chilworth. I wonder if our new Assistant Medical Officer will take part. Oh girl! What fun we should have if you were to play "Ann"! When I know I am going to see you again in a few weeks' time, I can keep composure but it is this not knowing when we will meet that floors me.

I have been thinking with gratitude today of all those people who have had the making of you. Your parents, that Ladies College in Hereford, those honest, good humoured, hardworking, Devonshire farmers in your ancestry. I would like to thank them. Does that sound ridiculous?

I stayed in the Chapel this morning after everyone had left and sat in that silent space for a long time, thinking of you. Some might think it blasphemous that I sit in a consecrated building, filled with desire, but to me everything about our love is holy. There is nothing between the two of us of which I am ashamed. You give my life meaning. You make me a better man than I am. I am filled with joy when I think of you.

Bless you

Mac

Darling Flo

Are you warm enough? Your house is very beautiful and very old but oh so cold in the winter.

It rained for the entire time I was with you in Devon in the summer and it has rained all autumn as well. I am glad to be busy, otherwise I would become quite melancholy in this grey, dripping weather without Flo at my side.

I ordered from the bookshop in Cambridge a book of poems by W B Yeats, the Irish poet, and it arrived in the post yesterday. In the first poem, it seemed that the poet was speaking directly to me, reminding me of memories which can never be taken from me and which will warm me in the winter rain – memories of halcyon summer days with you in years past, nudging away the bitterness of separation.

> I have heard the pigeons of the Seven Woods
> Make their faint thunder, and the garden bees
> Hum in the lime-tree flowers; and put away
> The unavailing outcries and the old bitterness
> That empty the heart.

Do you remember my reading you his poem which starts, "When you are old and grey and full of sleep"? It reminds me so of you. "the soft look your eyes had once" – "But one man loved the pilgrim soul in you". My darling Flo, off on her cycling expeditions!

We must live life so fully, completely that there is no space left for mourning. But, as for you, you know all my

197

thoughts and my desires. I can hold them up like a glass of water and they are clear and catch the sun.

Dear, lovely girl

Mac

Darling Girl

Dr Grogan arrived on Friday as I was in the middle of a rehearsal for *Liberty Hall*. The door of the hall opened and a tall lady wearing a sensible looking brown coat and skirt and a little black hat stood in the doorway looking intensely interested in what was going on on the stage. I was about to halt the rehearsal but she called out not to stop – that she would be quite happy sitting watching until we were finished.

I think she is going to be fun to work with. I showed her her quarters which are a little on the small side and she said, "It's a jolly good thing I didn't bring a cat, isn't it?" I was about to inform her that staff are not allowed to have pets when she added, "to swing, you know..." Her voice has a lilt of the Irish in it. I do hope you will be able to meet her one day.

I was hoping to get her to join us on stage for the performance at Christmas, but she says her forte is in organising not acting. She produced a play at Mullingar Asylum where until recently she was in charge of the women's wing.

She tells me she loves to walk, so if Dr Rogers permits us both to be absent from the asylum at the same time, I will introduce her to Fulbourn Fen and my tame ornithologist, Humble Evans.

One of the male patients who suffers from mania has been very calm for the past week or so – almost normal. I have been able to have a sensible conversation with him. Unfortunately, he is now starting to become excitable again and this morning he was shouting and laughing loudly during breakfast and had to be taken away before this affected the other patients. His wife never fails the fortnightly visit allowed from relatives. It is a tragic case because when he is in a sane phase, he is an intelligent, thoughtful man. I think the family cannot afford a private asylum.

I am being called and must put down my pen, but I am never beyond thought of you.

Your Mac

Darling Flo

Yesterday I noticed that Dr Grogan was scribbling away in a pad on her knee. I asked her what she was doing. She had drawn an entire skeleton from memory – from the feet up! Amazing! She put it down to the fact that when she was a child her father had asked her every day to draw what she had seen on her walks.

It makes one realise what a responsibility parents have for the development of their children. Coming to parenthood later in life than is usual, as will be the case with us, we may have more than other married couples to offer our children. I hope so.

Darling, we miss each other but we are immensely lucky in what we give each other – ideas, companionship, a sense of purpose, inspiration, a sharing of beauty, a distant voice that is always encouraging. I would not give up any of these. These come from you and make my heart beat. How often do we not appreciate the blessings that we have?

This brings you my love as always.

Mac

Darling Flo

You ask how old Dr Grogan is. According to her references she was born in 1864 – three years older than you and five years younger than myself. Some wag amongst the nurses has christened her "Dr Pat" because she comes from Wicklow in Ireland, so we are "Dr Pat" and "Dr Mac" when the nurses and the assistants think we are not listening. I rather miss my female patients now that Dr Grogan is taking care of them, but my work is very much easier with her here.

Dr Rogers and his sister are unsure of how to take Dr Grogan's humour. Many a time I have had to hide my laughter behind my napkin at luncheon. She has certainly lightened the atmosphere at Fulbourn.

"Dr Pat" asked me the other day if I ever doubted whether the "voices" heard by some of our patients were real – that is, whether they are in fact not mental illness but spiritual manifestations. I told her that when she has seen as many of these cases as I have, she will begin to see a pattern and it will become clear to her that this hearing of voices is a part of mental illness, however real it may seem to the patient.

There is one patient on the women's ward who hears her husband's voice when he is not there, and sees his figure out of the corner of her eye. When the mania is at its most intense, the poor woman feels his hands around her neck and screams out that she is being strangled. There is very little we can do in these cases apart from sedation. It is upsetting for everyone.

Well, there is very little of the lover about this letter.
But you know I am yours, always
Mac

My Darling

You are an amazing woman! You never cease to surprise me and touch me. No one else would have written as you did to her fiancé. Most women would be possessive, but you say – "Be happy!" Have I told you lately that I adore you?

I feel very flattered that you think Dr Grogan would be interested in me, but even if she were, my heart is yours, now and always. Never ever doubt that I love you. You say she would understand my work better than you could. For nearly eight years now you have been my loyal, loving comrade – what more could I want?

You wrote your letter at two in the morning. That is always a time for the goblins. The light of day would have shown you our certainty in each other. I love you so much, girl. But if one day, you should love someone else and have a chance of married happiness, then you know I should want you to be happy.

I am proud to say that you are "my" betrothed, but that does not mean that I own you, or you I. Things are not like that between us. We love each other because we want to do so. That is the joy and freedom that we give each other. We are like swifts, flying wing tip to wing tip – nothing binds us together but we trace the same pattern in the sky.

In my excitement over your letter and my desire to answer it, I very nearly forgot to tell you that my birthday present arrived from you safely a few days ago and I opened it this morning. It is a beautiful photograph, dearest. The one I carry in my waistcoat pocket is getting worn away with kissing but now I have a framed picture of my darling girl on my bedside table, to greet me smilingly when I open my eyes in the morning. Thank you.

Never, never doubt that I love you. If you do, you will have me to reckon with.

Yours, till a' the seas gang dry, my dear, and the rocks melt wi' the sun

Mac

Happy Christmas, My Flo! Have you made any new resolutions for 1904? Are you going to take up hockey, or perhaps ladies' football, like the aptly named Miss Honeyball whose photograph was in the paper today? I believe you to be capable of anything.

Dr Pat made the suggestion to our Medical Superintendent that the nurses form a hockey team but this was not well received, as you can imagine! Dr Rogers has firm ideas about team sports making ladies too masculine. I then rather naughtily suggested I order some Indian clubs for the patients to use, and he gave me a withering look while Dr Pat was struggling not to laugh.

Dr Pat told me the other day of an incident she experienced while working at Mullingar Asylum, where she caught two nurses abusing a young girl patient. The girl was not being violent, just noisy and abusive. One of the nurses held her while the other hit her on the back and made her cry. Dr Grogan told the nurses she would report them and it ended up with their being prosecuted which is just as it should be. Dr Grogan said if a nurse cannot control her temper, she should not be in her profession. Hear hear!

I hope the Christmas service at the Cathedral was inspiring. I should have liked to have sat next to you and held your hand. Do you suppose anyone would have noticed?

My darling girl – I have been laughing over your letter where you say you suggest I join you in your habit of taking a cold bath. This sounds a trifle indelicate. I do, in fact, often indulge in a cold bath in the morning, but this is more of a necessity than a virtue as the plumbing at

Fulbourn leaves much to be desired. Dr Grogan brought up the matter with Dr Rogers. He was horribly embarrassed and suggested she speak with Mr Miller. I don't think Dr Rogers believes ladies exist below the collar line. My Flo – I love you both above and below the collar line, more than you can know.

This is my ninth Asylum Christmas. I should very much like to try a family Christmas. I imagine our little house hung with greenery and red berries, the children decorating the tree, a warm fire and my dearest Flo.

In the meantime, I wish you the happiest of days, and my warmest good wishes to your family.

Yours always

Mac

PS Do you think, just occasionally, when we are married, we could take a HOT bath, and take it together?

22nd May 1904

Darling Flo

I have had a very interesting letter from Sydney Rowland. Do you remember my telling you about the brothers Lumiere – Auguste and Louis – and their attempts in colour photography? I remember it vividly because it was only the second time we had met and I must have bored you to death talking about photography. Poor girl!

The Lumieres had then just published an article on their experiments in colour photography. Rowland tells me they have now given a presentation of their process to the French Academy of Science. I won't bore you with details (not because I doubt your ability to understand) but it means we will be able to use our existing cameras to take colour photographs. Oh, how I should love to take a colour photograph of you, my Flo! I do hope the process becomes commercially viable soon.

It has set me remembering the dark room we made at Hele years ago. Do you remember? The scent of your hair, your voice beside me in the darkness. The memory of those intimate moments makes me long to be near you now.

I must be sensible.

I have to report that a patient, Henry S., escaped from the morning walking party, but was found half an hour later in the hedge so all was well. And you will be pleased to hear that the Committee have agreed to grant some space for the Medical Officer to keep his motorcycle and sidecar. Hurrah!

Your obedient (and loving) servant

Mac

My ain dear Flo

I had a new passenger in my wicker sidecar yesterday – Sydney Rowland. Of course, he was much more interested in taking the bicycle to pieces to "improve its going" than in actually riding in the sidecar! He seemed to enjoy himself very much and was covered in oil in no time. He tells me he is going to be part of a commission from the Lister going out to investigate plague. You would not imagine that plague was still a problem these days, but there was an outbreak in Glasgow not long ago, and two years ago half a million people died of it in India, according to Rowland. He wanted to pump me for information about life in India.

Rowland brought a friend with him – a geologist called Professor David – and the three of us sat in my little study last night, talking and laughing, until the air grew thick with smoke from our pipes and I had to throw the window open. Sydney and I listened, entranced, as David spoke of his expedition to Ellice Island a few years ago. He is a man of great wit and quiet charm – the most courteous person I have ever met. Rowland is obviously very taken with the professor, but we both had to remonstrate with David when he started to sing traditional songs in Tuvaluan.

Earlier in the evening, we all had dinner with Dr Rogers and his sister. The subject of the suffragettes came up in conversation. Dr Rogers said he felt that equality of political rights would destroy the beautiful ideal of womanhood, and the old chivalry of men to women – that it would lead to an effeminate nation. I saw Miss Annie nodding her head. Rowland, however, said that his brother-in-law, Mr Philip Gibbs, had been in London while there was a demonstration for "Votes for Women", and had seen the police treating some mill girls with brutality, tearing down their hair and winding it round their throats – his brother-in-law had said chivalry to women was not remembered then. Dr Rogers looked rather taken aback!

I can't help being glad, my love, that you and Mabel are interested in the NUWSS rather than in a more militant group, and that you believe in a peaceful approach to the question of suffrage. I would never try to dissuade you from doing what your conscience demands of you or to turn back from a path out of fear, but the idea of your being in danger and I so far away is unbearable to me. I want so much to take care of you and defend you from any harm.

With so much love

Your Mac

PS I'm sorry to hear that Hewitt has sold his motor cycle. I had hoped he and I could ride our motorcycles together one day.

My Darling Girl

I wish you the happiest of birthdays.

I hope you like the enclosed. I was browsing in Macmillan and Bowes yesterday. Mr Bowes happened to be there. He knows I like poetry and pointed out this newly printed compilation. The name on the cover is Laurence Hope but Mr Bowes told me that the author is in fact a woman – Adela Nicholson. She was born and lived in India, married to a man twice her age – like Etta Moore. I found a little corner of the bookshop to sit quietly and read some of the poems. For a wee while I was not in Cambridge at all but in my native India, listening to the passionate singing of love songs in Pashto or Urdu. I am sure some of her poetry is translated from these songs. They made me suddenly so homesick. And then there are poems which are clearly her own and these made me homesick for you. "Listen, my Beloved" – was one of these.

'Sometimes I think my longing soul remembers
A previous love to which it aims and strives,
As if this fire of ours were but the embers
Of some wild flame burnt out in former lives.
Perchance in earlier days I did attain
That which I seek for now so all in vain,
Maybe my soul with thine was fused and wed
In some great night, long since dissolved and dead.

Or has my spirit a divine prevision
Of vast vague passions stored in days to be,
When some strong souls shall conquer their division

And two shall be as one, eternally?
Finding at last upon each other's breast,
Unutterable calm and infinite rest,
While love shall burn with such intense a glow
That both shall die, and neither heed or know.'

I rashly bought two copies of the book, one for you and
one for me, and here is yours

    With my love Mac

Darling Flo

We are having an epidemic of influenza. It appears to be very infectious and of a particularly virulent type. I hope that it is nothing more sinister. The young male Attendant, Charles Richmond, was one of the first to succumb on 2nd April, and he is still confined to his room.

Dr Rogers is very unwell indeed and has taken to his bed. He refuses to allow Miss Annie near him in case she catches influenza, and he is looked after by his personal servant.

And among all this chaos, you write to me, saying that you love the Laurence Hope poetry book I sent you for your birthday, and you quote from "Song of Ramesram Temple Girl":

> 'I am a rose awaiting thee
> That none have touched or kissed.'

Oh, my darling, you cannot know how privileged I feel that it is so.

Forgive this short letter. You will understand. You always understand.

Your Mac

Sunday 23rd April 1905

My Darling

Forgive me if my letters are somewhat sporadic at present. There are grave concerns that the epidemic of influenza we have been having has been masking typhoid. I have reported to the Medical Officer of Health and await his report. Dr Rogers is very ill and so I am having to take charge. We have had nearly 50 patients attacked by it. Seven have died. The post-mortems on six of them showed typhoid fever.

We are becoming shorthanded as the disease spreads among the Attendants, and I am having to ask the Committee if I can engage more staff. I have also asked for a new copper so that all our milk may be boiled.

I try to appear calm and in control of the situation but it is very worrying. It would be difficult enough in an ordinary hospital, but in a mental asylum there is also the fear that without adequate supervision, patients may harm themselves or others. I feel if I take my eye off the situation for a moment, it may explode. And then there is simply the huge amount of work it entails – doing my own work as well as Dr Rogers', and on top of that putting into place precautions to prevent the enteric fever spreading.

The Attendants are working wonderfully well but, as you can imagine, they need supervision and reassurance. I sleep in a little room off one of the infirmaries so as to be on hand, and I use Dr Roger's office during the day time. There are constantly knockings at my door, questions to be answered, papers to be signed, decisions to be made.

Only the thought of your steadfast love so many miles away keeps me sane.

God bless you

Mac

PS My protégé, the Attendant, Charles Richmond, has left his room at last after contracting the disease at the beginning of April. He was ill for such a long time that I was beginning to worry that he would not pull through.

Darling Flo

I am so sorry not to have replied to your letters. Be assured that I treasure them and they are the one bright star in my otherwise clouded sky, although the epidemic, I think, is on the wane. Dr Rogers is better but still not back at work.

We lost Alice Roberts last Tuesday. She was a Night Attendant. She was a good worker with compassion, a great deal of common sense and a nice sense of humour. I liked her. On Monday evening, she seemed to be turning the corner. Her fever had abated somewhat; she was quite lucid and returned my smile when I took her pulse. I thought by morning, we would see an improvement, but about 3.00 a.m. one of the Attendants called me to say she had slipped away.

The world should know of these brave people who continue to do their duty in spite of the dangers.

All my love

Mac

Darling Flo

I am so angry I can hardly write. Although we have not had the results of the tests yet on the asylum farm milk, I am fairly certain that that is where the source of the infection lies. I gave written orders that milk from the asylum cows was <u>not</u> to be used in case of dangerous contamination. A member of the Farm Committee has been sending me letters and irresponsibly interfering with my orders. I have written a steaming report to the Committee saying that I need support and not hectoring. There is no question of my knuckling down to this person. The safety of too many people is at stake.

I am taking this opportunity, too, to put pressure on the Committee about the building of an isolation block. I have put the plans before them. It should cost around £550 with asylum labour. It is desperately needed if we are to combat infectious diseases. I sincerely trust we may not contract scarlet fever, but by jingo, if we do!

We need more accommodation for the Attendants too, and we are under pressure for those living in Cherry Hinton to sleep in at the asylum rather than carry infection to their homes. It is understandable, but where on earth am I to put them?

Sweetheart, you deserve a more loverlike letter than this, but I can think of nothing else except the epidemic. I will say, though, that you must try to get your father to rest. He must leave charity work to those who have the strength for it. Tell him that his future son-in-law who is a medical man and knows what he is talking about, insists upon it!

My love always, always

Mac

Darling Flo

I am glad to hear that your father is feeling better. You are a good nurse. Your services are needed here, dear one, for we are very short-staffed.

Arthur Bell, our carpenter, has died of typhoid. He always built the scenery for our Christmas performances with great imagination and good will. Young Sidney Thorne, Mr Thorne's son, is convalescing and doing well, thank heaven. He is the apple of his father's eye. I had to send a report to the Commissioners in Lunacy. Thirteen patients have died, and 37 are convalescing. One of the female Attendants has died – Alice Roberts whom I told you of – the other Attendants who caught the disease are convalescing.

I have had more trouble with the farm people. Noble, the stockman for the asylum farm, was supposed to be supervising two of the patients working for him – Green and Lawrence. But they were seen to be freely drinking the raw contaminated drink entrusted to them to be thrown on the furnace. Lawrence drank the milk until he vomited. The next day they were again seen to be drinking the milk. I was a few minutes too late to witness it. Thank goodness they don't seem to have contracted the disease but the irresponsibility of the man, Noble, is unbelievable. I hope he is taken to account.

I have been working on a scheme whereby our convalescing Attendants, and those who have been having extra work during the epidemic, can have a few weeks paid holiday. The Hunstanton Convalescent Home will be happy to take them – one guinea for three weeks plus

5/- for food. The Committee have agreed. Hooray! The Attendants all thoroughly deserve it. There was a little delay in the arrangements as I had a slight disagreement with Miss Conway, the Head Female Attendant, as to whether or not one of the female Attendants should be included. Miss Conway is very touchy lately. It is not surprising after all that we have been through.

Some of the staff will get a week's holiday, some two weeks and some three. It is difficult to say who is more entitled than another. Those working in the laundry and infirmaries have had more work to do, but there is the man who helps at the post-mortems, the man who carries the excreta, those working shorthanded in the kitchen. And what scheme can I devise for Mr Archer, Miss Conway, Mr Thorne, Mr Miller, Dr Grogan – who individually labour to lighten my work?

Yours always

Mac

Darling Flo

The Committee have offered to give me a cheque as a reward for what they call "special services" during the epidemic. A gentleman does not expect a monetary reward for doing his duty. I have told them that I would rather not accept it. Of course, what I really need is a few weeks' leave so that I can have my energies recharged by time with my girl. Sadly, I think that is not going to happen.

Yes, I have to admit that I still feel very tired, but it is only to be expected. You must not worry about me, girl. You have more than enough to worry about with the needs of your own family.

Dr Pat has suggested she take over the organising of the Christmas entertainment this year, which is a relief. I shall sit at the back of the hall while they rehearse, and make rude remarks.

This afternoon for the first time in months, I was able to get to the Fen. I drove myself in the pony and trap, not wanting to scare the birds with the noise of my motor bicycle. I could hear your voice telling me to wrap up warm, so I did, and was quite cosy at first in the hide. After a while, the cold started to seep in and I got up to go, and at that moment I caught sight of a short-eared owl. The first I have seen this year.

Do you remember, years ago, the first time I came to stay with you in Devon, we went out walking and I talked to you about birds? What a very strange lover you must have thought me! When you think of it, we actually have spent very little time physically together. Our love has been written in letters. Perhaps our great grandchildren will find our letters one day in a dusty attic and be shocked at how their progenitors behaved. I do hope so.

Take care of yourself, sweetheart, as I am not there to do it.

Love

Mac

LETTER TO MISS CHAVE FROM
DR GERTRUDE GROGAN

Sunday 3rd December 1905

Dear Miss Chave

My name is Gertrude Grogan and I work with your fiancé, Dr McCutchan, known to everyone here at Fulbourn as "Dr Mac".

I'm sorry to have to tell you that he is quite seriously ill at the moment. His doctor has ordered complete rest and will not allow him paper and pen even, so Dr Mac has asked me to write to you because he feels you may worry when you do not hear from him.

A few days ago, he collapsed while doing his rounds of the wards and was taken to his room. Dr Nicholls – our local doctor in the village – a good man and well respected – says it is a problem with his heart and intends to consult with the heart specialist, Professor Allbutt, so you can be reassured that Dr Mac is in the best of hands.

He is not in a great deal of pain as long as he lies still, but is dizzy when he tries to stand. He says occasionally that his muscles ache and he has fluid retention in his legs which bothers him somewhat, but he spends more time asking about what is going on in the asylum than he does in complaining. I tell you these things because I know, if I were his fianceé, I would like to know the exact truth.

Dr Mac confided in me about his engagement to you, and the fact that it is not generally known. Please be assured that I shall treat this as strictly confidential.

I am very happy to answer any questions you may have and to pass on messages to Dr Mac. When he had his attack and was lying in bed, awaiting the arrival of Dr Nicholls, he said to me – "If this should be the end, tell Flo I thought of her now!" Of course, it was not the end, but I thought you would like to know.

With warmest regards

Dr A. Gertrude Grogan

Monday 18th December 1905

Dear Miss Chave

Your warm, gaily coloured travel rug arrived today. Dr Mac has been allowed to sit in his armchair for short periods and at these times he insists upon having your rug tucked around him. I wish you could have seen his face when he opened the parcel. I think if I had not been there, he would have wept. He was more moved than I have ever seen him.

Professor Allbutt has seen him and is of the opinion that he is suffering from dilatation of the heart and he must exert himself as little as possible for the present. He feels Dr Mac will be unfit to take further duty for some months at least. The Committee met today and have granted him three months' leave of absence as soon as he is fit to travel. Perhaps in a little while he will be well enough to come and visit you.

I think he is now feeling less worried about how the asylum is running without him, and he enjoys seeing visitors, although we keep these to a minimum lest he become tired. The Attendants all want to see him. Mr Thorne came and gave at Dr Mac's bedside a rendition of the song he is to sing at the Christmas entertainment. Miss Annie brings gruel of her own concoction which we subsequently (shhh!) empty into the sink as Dr Mac says it is quite inedible!

But she means well. And everyone brings what they can to make him feel better. He is very much missed.

With best wishes for the Christmas season.

Yours sincerely

Gertrude Grogan

Sunday 31st December 1905

My Darling Flo

It is the last day of the old year. Thank you for this year. What it would have been like without you I cannot bear to contemplate. Your letters and your love have sustained me through all the trials of 1905. I wish that you could say the same to me but I fear the giving has been all upon one side.

I feel better, and that old tyrant, Dr Nicholls, has allowed me writing materials at long last. I think we must face the fact, sweetheart, that I will never be completely strong, but as long as I can work and win you for my own – that is all I care about. I shall be a very good patient and do as I am told, if only I can achieve that.

The Head of the Female Attendants, Miss Conway, leaves today. Her health was broken down by overwork during the epidemic. We have not always seen eye to eye, but she is a good woman and will be missed.

I am sitting in my armchair, with your rug around me. I feel as if I am in your arms. I love you so very much.

I want for you the best of times in 1906. I want you to go gloriously out into the world, doing great things and having fun, and not worrying too much about this old crock, but always remembering that he loves you. I want you to feel the glow of my love about you as you cycle around Hereford. When you are sad, just remember, "Mac loves me" and feel happy again.

My pen travels more slowly than my thoughts, and my hand is too tired to keep up.

I will write again.

Be happy.

Mac

My Darling Flo

I love the idea of our thinking of each other at Angelus time. It is twenty minutes to eleven now so I have one hour and twenty minutes to get ready for you. Stand very still at 12 o'clock and afterwards you must write and tell me where I kissed you.

A chap with a bad heart must not become too excited, however.

Do you remember I refused the cheque that was offered me for "special services" during the epidemic? Dr Pat said that she would refuse hers if I refused mine so in the end I swallowed my pride and accepted it. It may come in handy if I am ever fit enough to travel to Hereford to see you. Dr Allbutt, the specialist, is still advising me to keep to my room. I have become very tired of the view from my bed and armchair.

I am now able to read, however. Until now, Dr Pat has been kindly reading to me as even holding a book was too much like hard work. Such a wreck you have as a lover! I asked her to read some Burns poetry. Rabbie Burns in the vernacular with an Irish accent is very funny! And she read me some of Adela Nicholson's poetry. It brought you very near.

Dr Nicholls is at the door with his stethoscope instrument so I must finish now.

Keep free of coughs and colds. Wrap up warm. Doctor's orders!

Love

Mac

10

10th April 1906

Dear Miss Chave

Little did I realise when I wrote to tell you how ill Dr Mac has been during the last fortnight, that it would result in your brother's arrival here! It is such a relief! Dr Nicholls is very efficient but he has a practice to take care of and can only make short, infrequent visits. It makes a huge difference to have Dr Chave on hand every moment of the day. He took the asylum by storm! Whatever objections Dr Rogers raised, he simply waved them away and proceeded to take charge of the situation.

The effect upon Dr Mac has been amazing. The idea of your brother leaving his practice in Cardiff and travelling all the way to Fulbourn to take care of him has overwhelmed him.

I know your brother will be sending you reports of Dr Mac's progress but do write to me if you have any questions. I have come to value our correspondence for its own sake.

Many good wishes

Gertrude Grogan

Tuesday 17th April 1906

Dear Miss Chave

Dr Mac was well enough to be moved to the Nurses Hostel in Cambridge today and your brother is on his way back to Cardiff. I think it is not too much of an exaggeration to say that your brother saved his life by coming here to look after him. Dr Chave told me that his wife is Irish and they were married in Cork. I have an invitation to visit them in Cardiff if ever I am travelling in that direction. He is a charming man. I should very much like to call upon them.

I hope to visit Dr Mac in the Hostel, but with my duties here at the Asylum, I may not be able to see him as often as I would like. Be assured that I will let you know how he does, however.

With best wishes

Gertrude Grogan

Darling Flo

I cannot believe how quiet it is here. At the asylum, there are always patients crying out and shouting. Here, all is calm. The nurses are very kind. I am on the ground floor and can see out into the garden and watch the birds.

It is eight years today since I gave you your engagement ring. I remember you were very serious when I slipped it onto your finger, and then you looked up at me and I kissed you. The good thing about our being so much apart is that I can remember every one of your kisses.

Darling, have I thanked you for saving my life? For that is what you did by asking your brother to come to Fulbourn. I had been through a bad time and I remember thinking that if Death could take away the pain and fatigue and discomfort, then I would be very pleased for Him to do it. Then Tom was suddenly there, giving me hope and relief from pain. I think when we first met, he was not happy at the idea of our getting engaged, was he? Your sister, Ivy, had recently married and was living at the other side of the world, and here was this foreigner (for such he must have thought me) about to steal his big sister away too. I think we have a better understanding of each other now. He is a fine doctor and a good man. You must be very proud of him.

I am better, much better. I hope soon to be able to travel and come to see my Flo.

So much love

Mac

Darling Flo

You cannot imagine what it meant to me to hear your beloved voice! I had no idea what was to come when my nurse said she had a surprise for me and wheeled me out into the hall to the telephone. I can still hear your excited voice saying, "Hello Mac, darling, it's me – Flo!" If anything could cure my poor old heart, it would be to hear your voice.

Was it you who persuaded your father to have a telephone installed? I am sure that it was. My intrepid, wonderful girl!

To know that I can speak to you makes such a difference.

I love you very much. Have I told you lately?

Yours always

Mac

Darling Flo

I cannot tell you what it has meant to me to be able to hear your voice on the telephone, but now I want to write to you so that you will have my words to keep.

You see, I have a presentiment that this might be my last letter to you. If it turns out not to be the case, then we can laugh over it together in the years to come, but I fear it will be otherwise. The symptoms I was experiencing in December and March have returned. I want to write to you now in case the time comes when picking up the pen is too difficult.

We once agreed that thanks between us were unnecessary, and I cannot thank you, I can only rejoice in the fact that you exist, and that you, out of everyone I have ever known, have been that one special person for me. I adore you.

Being natural, being open, being breathless with excitement in each other's presence – these have marked us; these have given the last eleven years a validity which I cannot believe but I shall carry with me for ever. How little we know, but I have come to believe that what is wholly good and pure cannot be destroyed. John Donne thought that whatever was mixed equally would survive. Our love will survive. We shall meet again –

'Finding at last upon each other's breast,
Unutterable calm and infinite rest.'

We belong to each other. To others too, of course, but then love is not a fabric that becomes the smaller by sharing. Loving you has taught me that.

I am loath to finish this. Never finished. Never. Remember. We love for ever. Semper.

Always

Mac

Dear Miss Chave

You told me that you were relying upon me to let you know if the worst should happen. This is a difficult letter for me to write. Our dear Dr Mac passed away this afternoon, just after 2 o'clock. I went to see him yesterday. The Chaplain had just visited him.

After the difficulties he has had over the last few days, he seemed not to be suffering. He said he was not afraid of what was to come. All that worried him was that he was going to cause you pain. He asked me to tell you always to remember how much he has loved you and that he wanted you to live a full and happy life here until he met you again. I held his hand, and he thanked me for being a good friend. I think you have intuitively known that I would have been more than a good friend to him had his heart not belonged to you. As I knew it could never be, I was happy to be his friend. It was a privilege. I shall never forget him, his kindness, his wisdom, his humour. The patients loved him because they knew he understood what it was like to be poor, and alone, and frightened. The staff knew they could always rely upon his kindness.

I am going to give my resignation to the Committee. I cannot bear to continue working at the Asylum without him.

I feel so much for you. My own bereavement is great, but yours must be indescribable.

With very best wishes

Gertrude Grogan

The Lodge
Dunbur Rd
Wicklow
Ireland

20th December 1930

Dear Miss Chave

My sister, Dr Gertrude Grogan, died unexpectedly earlier this year while staying at Tegernsee in Bavaria. She appointed me her executor and while I was looking through her papers, I found this letter from you. At first glance, it looked very personal, and it obviously meant a great deal to her. My sister has had a roving life and has always "travelled light", but she has kept this for 26 years. You will think I am foolish, but I have been unable to throw it away. I have decided to return it to you to do with as you will.

Please be assured, I have read only the first line.

With all good wishes

George Meredyth Grogan

Moor House
Widemarsh Common
Hereford
Herefordshire

24th September 1906

Dear Gertrude

It is three months since our Dr Mac left us. I still feel that he is very near to me, but for all that, I am lonely, and I should dearly like to talk to someone about him.

You and I shared Mac's last months together. I think you will understand how I feel. My brothers and sisters were fond of Mac – especially Tom, as you know – but they have always thought the situation was unfair on me and that Mac caused me unhappiness. That is quite, quite false, but it means that it is difficult to confide in them. My parents say that as we kept the engagement a secret for eight years, it would be foolish to publicise it now. They feel if I am not encouraged to talk about Mac, then I will forget him and be happy. I want never to forget him.

I have Mac's letters and his photographs, but oh, how I need to hear his voice! And most of all to feel the love between us. It is that feeling which is what I am afraid I will forget.

I remember the first time I saw him in the garden at Moor House in the autumn of 1894. I wonder if he ever told you how his connection with our family came about. Probably not, as it shows him to some advantage and he was an unassuming man. The first time we heard of him was about three years before we actually met.

It was my sister, Ivy, who literally fell over him in Chester. She was fifteen years old, and attending a school run by some cousins of ours in Bowdon in Cheshire. She and my cousin, Miss Edith Lang, had taken the train to Chester to meet up with some friends and were walking along the main street when Ivy stumbled and would have fallen into the road in front of an approaching horse and cart had not Mac caught her arm and pulled her back. Mac was working as a Medical Assistant in Somerset at the time but had been paying a visit to his friend, Dr Morrison, in nearby Wrenbury and it was fortunate that he and Dr Morrison were passing. They insisted on inviting Ivy and my cousin into a tea shop to make sure she was uninjured. In the course of the conversation, Dr Morrison discovered that Ivy's home was in Hereford, and he told her that he was soon to take up a post as Assistant Medical Officer in the asylum there.

I was in Australia with my parents at the time. My father had been left some property in Queensland by a cousin and he had to go over to inspect it. Ivy wrote to tell us of her little adventure and when we arrived home in Hereford, we discovered that Dr Morrison had taken up the position at Burghill Asylum. My parents invited him to dinner in order to thank him for what he had done for Ivy. He told them that in fact it was Mac who had saved Ivy from being run down but he was very pleased to come to dinner, being a bachelor, and often visited Moor House, so that we came to know him quite well.

In September 1894, another post of Assistant Medical Officer became vacant at Burghill Asylum and Dr Morrison invited Mac to stay for a few days in order to have an interview and see over the asylum. He brought him to Moor House. I remember watching Mac walk across the lawn to where my parents, Ivy and I were sitting having tea. I did not think of him in terms of a prospective husband at the time. He was ten years older than me, which seemed more important then than it did later.

I had the impression of a man who was neatly dressed and slender, but with rather plump little cheeks and a dark complexion. I found out later that his father's ancestors came from Nantes, in France.

I was aware of his looking at me rather intently, but then was distracted by the fact that the maid came running out of the house to say that Billie, my cockatoo, had escaped again and I had to rush indoors to try to catch him.

Mac told me later that he was attracted to me right away. He said the look of panic on my face made him want to laugh, and he felt a comradeship with me. He liked the energetic way I ran into the house. Such little things to have such a momentous outcome.

He spoke to my father that day about his great interest in photography, and asked whether father would like him to take pictures of the family. Father was keen for him to do so, and two days later Mac arrived with his camera and made us pose in the garden, at a window, standing, sitting etc. He was very demanding!

He started work at the asylum at Burghill in December. We saw a good deal of him. That winter was particularly mild, I remember, and he joined my friends and myself on our cycle rides.

I hardly had time to get to know him very well, however, as the following month we went out to Queensland again to visit my father's sheep station. Mac had asked if he could write to me, and during those two years while I was out of the country, we corresponded. His letters were always very proper! He came from a well-to-do family in the Indigo trade in India but with his father's failing health and his elder brother's unexpected death, the family had had financial difficulties, and Mac was aware from the start of my father's position in society, and the gulf between my fortune and his. I have to admit that I was flattered that a gentleman should be interested in me. I had become resigned to the fact that I would be the one in my family to stay at home and look after my dear parents, but a woman never quite gives up hope that she will get married and have a home of her own and children one day.

On returning from Queensland in the spring of 1897, I only saw Mac a few times before we left to spend the summer in Devon. My father suffers poor health and we generally spend our summers there. So, there we were again, having to correspond by letter. Mac came down to visit us. I still did not feel I knew him very well, and he accepted that he was fonder of me than I was of him, but in February 1898, when I returned to Hereford, we became engaged. My immediate family knew but no one else.

It is strange that sometimes we do not recognise our own feelings. It was not until April 1898 that I realised how much he had come to mean to me. I had to accompany my parents to Malvern so that my father could take the waters there. Just before we left, I had news that Mac was seriously ill with influenza. I had to leave Hereford without knowing how he was. Then I had a letter from him, saying he was convalescing and all was well. I remember running upstairs with the letter and, much to my own surprise, bursting into tears in my bedroom. It was then that our love became perfectly balanced, equal on both sides.

His body became very dear to me. I grew to love the set of his shoulders, the way he wore his hat, the way he crossed his legs, his delicate hands, the feeling of his cheek against my own. Some would say it is indelicate for a female to write such things, but I believe that a woman experiences desire just as a man does. I remember once when Mac was staying with us – it was after he had moved to Cambridgeshire – my parents had gone out for the evening and we had the house to ourselves. I would have given myself to him then, but he said no, he loved and respected me too much. He said my parents trusted him and he would not betray that trust. Some people would say it was sad that we never "knew" each other in the biblical sense, but in a strange way, because we knew that we both desired it and would be happy to give ourselves one to the other, it was as if our physical union was happening continuously, joyfully, all the time.

After he moved to Fulbourn in 1902, we seldom saw each other, but through our letters we grew to know each other intimately. He was determined that we should not waste our lives by feeling sad that we were apart, but that our love should enrich our days and spill over to touch the people we lived with and the people we met. I am determined that this should continue to be so even now when there will be such a long wait until I see him again. I am nearly forty now – perhaps twenty or thirty years until we meet – until I hear his laugh again.

When Mac died, my family was sad for me. They did not understand how much happiness he gave me and still gives me. To love, and know that you are loved, is the finest feeling in the world.

Our correspondence during Mac's illness made me feel you were a person I could speak openly to about my feelings, but I hope this letter has not given you pain. Perhaps I am being selfish in writing to you like this. I know you loved him too. I think perhaps Mac was the only man you would have sacrificed your career for. It was not meant to be. You were meant for some other great purpose. I wish I could feel the same about myself, but I can only muddle on as reliable old Flo, and look after my dear parents and be an affectionate aunt. I should not repine. I have a loving family and adequate means and most of all, I have known what it is to be loved passionately. I am the most fortunate of women.

With grateful thanks

Florence M. Chave

PART 4 – RELEASE

26th September 1972

Dear Gwen

I am sitting here in tears, and for the first time in months it is not for myself but for Mac and Flo.

I went into the Record Office to look at those letters the workmen found in the attic, and Miss Jancey, the Archivist, very kindly said I could take them home to read. So, I have spent the evening reading Mac's letters to Flo. In one letter, Mac talks of hoping to get a job in Bristol – if he had got it, they might have been able to get married. There is a gap in the letters there (SO frustrating!) but he obviously didn't get the post. It's so cruel.

Before reading the letters, I hadn't been sure how Flo felt about Mac after 1898 (when her diary ends) but you can tell from what he says in his letters how she felt about him, and there is one letter – one precious letter of Flo's – which survived by an amazing chance. I knew that on Mac's part, he must have still loved her because he left her everything he had in the world. Now I know that Flo, too, felt the same.

It's so sad that they never married and had children. They would have been fantastic parents. You get the feeling, though, that just the fact that they loved each other affected their lives and how they reacted to people around them. Their love spilled over to Mac's patients, and the people he worked with, and to Flo's family and friends.

I hope they have found each other now.

Love

Jane

The Basement Flat
Albert House
Portland Street
Hereford

27th September 1972

Dear Gwen

I went to the library today to see if I could find out about some of the people Mac mentions in his letters. One of them was a doctor called Sydney Rowland. He was the son of the vicar at Stoke sub Hamdon. I remember cycling past the vicarage when we visited.

Rowland took the first mobile laboratory to France in 1914. Apparently, he had seen this state-of-the-art campervan-type machine at the Motor Show, and when war broke out, he thought it would be just the thing for a mobile laboratory, so he tracked it down, and he and his friends at the Lister (where he worked) ripped out all its luxury innards and transformed it into a laboratory. Rowland died in 1917 of meningitis – he was working on meningitis amongst the troops.

I found an obituary written by his boss, Charles Martin. I have copied it out for you:

"Sydney Rowland was a cheery, erratic creature, with a vivid zest in life. He had a fine imagination, towards which he was not always sufficiently critical. He was courageous, impulsive, sensitive, generous to a fault, withal casual and thoughtless; but in view of his many sterling qualities, his friends willingly put up with any shortcomings. He was a charming companion, and much beloved by those who knew him well. Especially he endeared himself to all those who had to work under him. He was a great favourite with children, and among those who will miss him most will be the many young people of his acquaintance."

I love the bit about Rowland not being sufficiently critical towards his imagination – leaping into conclusions with both feet! I think I am drawn to him because he reminds me of a certain cartoon artist.

Has Jenny started at St Mary's yet?

Much love

Jane

JANE'S DIARY

Thursday 28th September 1972

Maria rang this morning. About 2,000 prisoners will be released tomorrow! There will be a plane on standby to bring Hugh home.

Giles is being very good about my taking time off.

This time tomorrow night!

Friday 29th September 1972

I don't want to write it. If I don't write it, perhaps it won't be true. But it is true. Hugh is still in Salemba prison. Maria and I and Hugh's editor from the *Daily Sketch*, Peter Gosforth, drove to RAF Fairford early this morning, still not knowing exactly what time Hugh would arrive. We were kept supplied with coffee and sandwiches all day. The waiting would have been awful if we hadn't been so sure he was coming. Then an officer came into the room saying there was a phone call for Maria from Nicholas Mason at the Foreign Office. Maria went out to take it. Peter and I looked at each other. She came back in and her lips were trembling. I got her to sit down.

She took a minute to calm herself down and then told us what had happened. The British Ambassador had been waiting outside the prison with the official car. The doors opened and the prisoners started to stream out. The street was full of the prisoners' friends and families, hugging them and crying. But there was no sign of Hugh. Then a frail-looking Indonesian man came out of the prison, and approached the Embassy car. The man said he had a message from Hugh – that he wouldn't be coming home that day. He looked ill and frightened, and wanted to be taken to the British Embassy right away.

When he got to the Embassy, he explained that his name was Adika. He had been Hugh's guide and had been held in the same cell. Hugh had had no one to bring him parcels of food and bedding – the prison provides very little – and Adika's wife had brought what she could for both of them. Adika had got ill and had not been allowed to leave prison to go to hospital.

The prisoners due to be released were given a card with a number on it to hand in as they were let out the following day. Hugh thought that, with the number of men going through, there was a possibility that they wouldn't notice if Adika went out in his place. Hugh gave his card to Adika because he thought if Adika didn't get out now, in his weakened state he might not survive.

I don't know whether to be proud or angry. Yes, I do. I'm proud of him. But I want him back.

Sunday 1st October 1972

I went round to see Maria yesterday. She was on the phone to Mr Mason at the Foreign Office when I arrived.

He said the Embassy are arranging for Adika and his wife to come to England, to make sure they are safe before they ask for Hugh to be released. Maria has asked Mr Mason if she and I can talk with Adika.

Maria and I talked for hours. She told me what it was like when she first knew Hugh. She was very open about the fact that she persuaded him into marriage. She was dazzled by his talent. It was only after they had been together for a while that she realised she had acquired not just an artist, but a human being with ideas of his own. I asked her straight out if she was still in love with him. She said she loved him dearly in the way you would love a younger brother who needed looking after, but she didn't think it was in her to "fall in love". She said she liked her own company too much. I have come to feel very fond of her and it's a great relief to know without any doubt now that I am not taking Hugh away from her.

I rang Giles from the phone box this morning. He said not to worry about going in to work tomorrow. The weekend has been awful.

Tuesday 3rd October 1972

I didn't feel I could cope with the Crafty Christmas Club tonight but I couldn't very well not go, so I went.

Of course, they all wanted to know whether Hugh was home yet or not. Kim said she and her daughter had been watching out for it on the news but nothing had been said. I explained what had happened. There was a little silence and then they all started talking at once. Kartika was the only one who didn't say anything. She just stood there with tears in her eyes.

When I got home later that night, she arrived on my doorstep. She wanted to know where in England Adika and his wife were going to be taken, and, if necessary, to offer her services as an interpreter. I said I would pass that on. I hadn't thought about the language problem. It would be great to have Kartika there, and Adika would trust her because she knows them.

Wednesday 4th October 1972

Maria and Kartika and I are going to London tomorrow to see Adika. I took the bus out to Gwen's this evening, and told her about everything that has been happening. It was good to talk it through with her. My mind just doesn't seem to be working properly. I said to Maria, surely they will let Hugh out of prison when they know he is still in there? She said Nick Mason had said there was no saying what their attitude would be.

I so want to speak to Adika about Hugh, but at the same time I dread what he will say.

Thursday 5th October 1972

Adika and his wife, Sarah, were lovely. Very petite. Adika looked thin and ill, and you could see how the strain of the past few months had affected his wife, but they were full of smiles when we arrived and seemed really pleased to see us.

They couldn't get over Kartika being there and you could see the relief on their faces to see someone familiar and to be able to speak their own language. Adika's story took some time to tell as Kartika had to translate sentence by sentence. He said he had known he was in danger of arrest because his brother-in-law had been arrested a few months previously under suspicion of having communist connections. He and Hugh had been walking for a couple of days when they were stopped and taken into custody. They had both been interrogated, but not tortured. Maria and I looked at each other at this point. Torture was what we had both been dreading to hear.

They had ended up in a cell together in Salemba. We asked if it was just the two of them in the cell and he said no, it was a small cell with five inmates. It had one large raised platform and one small one – four people slept on the large one. Hugh, luckily for him, was taller than the other prisoners so he got the small platform to himself, but they only had one mat each for sleeping on and a pillow. The platforms were stone and really cold at night.

If Adika's wife hadn't sent in parcels with sacking and blankets, it would have been awful. A lot of the prisoners had respiratory problems.

I felt so grateful to Sarah. I don't suppose they have money to spare, and she was sending in parcels for both Adika and Hugh. I couldn't tell her what I felt so I just touched her hand, and she smiled at me.

They had no mosquito nets. Adika said that the mosquitoes were the worst problem – even worse than the bedbugs. He said the lights were kept on all night as part of security. You weren't allowed books – except the Bible and the Ku'ran – and you weren't allowed to read newspapers or listen to the wireless.

We asked him about the food. He said there wasn't much of it and the quality was bad. Two plates of rice a day and a small piece of soya cake and some spinach. They grew rice and spinach at the prison and if you helped with the growing of it, you sometimes got better food. You didn't get given anything else – no sugar, tea, coffee, fruit, fat – no soap. That was why they relied on parcels from home so much.

We asked him about Hugh. Was he well? How was he coping? Adika said sometimes he got down, like they all did, and he suffered from the poor diet, but that it was usually Hugh who made them laugh and kept their spirits up. One of the prisoners in their cell had fairly good English and would translate Hugh's jokes. He thought Hugh found the lack of privacy difficult, though.

The guards had discovered that he could draw cartoons and he would get extra food for his cellmates by drawing cartoons for them. Once he drew a cartoon of the superintendent and was put into solitary confinement for a month. In confinement, you were not allowed to receive food parcels and had to survive on what they gave you.

Adika said one of the worst things was that you were given no information as to what was going to happen to you, whether you would stand trial or just carry on in prison for years.

It was good to know the worst. I hope it was the worst. We couldn't help wondering if Adika was being kind and not telling us everything. Kartika said she thought the ill treatment of prisoners was not as bad as it used to be. Maria thanked her for coming. I felt at last, in finding Kartika, I had done SOMETHING to help.

Friday 6th October 1972

The worst of news. Maria came round this evening. She sat next to me on my knobbly sofa bed and told me. The Foreign Office have been in touch with the Indonesian authorities who are saying that as far as they are concerned, Hugh has been released and there is nothing further they can do. Mr Mason said they have explained the situation again and again, but come up against a brick wall. He has been told that the situation is delicate and it is not possible for more pressure to be applied at the moment.

I couldn't say anything. I sat not moving. Inside I felt I was going out of control with panic. For the first time the idea that Hugh might not come back became real to me.

Maria was saying that she has spoken to Peter, Hugh's editor, and he has been told by the Foreign Office not to push the matter. Even Maria seems not to know what to do now.

I keep thinking of Hugh in prison for years and years in those awful conditions with no hope.

Saturday 7th October 1972

Kartika came round to ask if there was any news about Hugh's release. She was very sympathetic but obviously not surprised.

After she left, I couldn't stand being on my own any longer and cycled to Gwen's. It was the most beautiful October day and as I cycled, I thought about Hugh keeping people's spirits up and drawing cartoons for the guards, and then I imagined him lying on cold stone all night. He's 43, not old but not young either.

Gwen, as always, made me feel better. I told her how the government was saying they couldn't do anything, and how powerless I felt. As I left, she said, "Sometimes individuals succeed where governments fail."

Sunday 8th October 1972

Giles came round to ask if I had thought of Amnesty International. He gave me a telephone number to ring.

Monday 9th October 1972

I went into work but Giles sent me home again. I rang Amnesty International from the phone box and talked to a friendly woman. She was very sympathetic, but she said that our Foreign Office has a better relationship with the Indonesian government than they do. They would be happy to take Hugh's case on but warned that it could be months before they get anywhere, if indeed they do.

Tuesday 10th October 1972

It was the last Christmas Crafty Club tonight. I nearly didn't go, but in the end I did and I'm so glad I did.

I got there a little late and I could see that Kartika had told them the bad news about Hugh. Nobody said anything though until after the elephants had all been named. I did feel proud of my class. They had produced a beautiful herd of elephants. Everyone voted Kim's elephant the best, and Alison even offered to sell it in her shop. Our sulky girl was quite transformed.

Then, when we stopped for coffee, Mavis said, "We are all so sorry about your Hugh, dear." And they all started talking at once. Felicity kept saying, "Why can't he come home?" Serena was the only one not talking. She had been quiet (for her!) all evening. She said, "So the government can't do anything?"

"So they say."

"It's up to you then. There must be loads of people out there who like Hugh's cartoons – why don't you get a petition up – take it to No 10 – MAKE them take notice?"

And they all started saying what a good idea it was. I had Gwen's "Sometimes individuals succeed ..." echoing in my head. Could I do it? What would Maria think? And how could I get publicity for it if Hugh's editor was not supposed to be getting involved?

Wednesday 11th October 1972

I couldn't sleep last night. I kept thinking up all sorts of snags to the scheme. Suppose I made things worse? Suppose Maria was really against it? Suppose nobody was interested in signing the petition? How exactly should I go about it?

Then Flo came into my mind. All through the last few months, I have felt her encouraging me on. She and her sisters were all so brave and forward thinking. Mabel had a university degree, taught in a school and joined the Suffragists. Ivy left her family and married a man the other side of the world. Flo cycled intrepidly all the way from Devon to Bristol, and got engaged to a penniless asylum doctor from India in spite of her family's doubts about him.

But in the end, Flo didn't marry him. In those days, you were admired if you waited patiently for your man to fight his way to a position where he could give you the life you were used to. It was prudent. It was virtuous. If Flo had known how long she would have to wait, though – if she had known that Mac would die so young – would she have decided to risk upsetting her family and shocking her friends, and insisted on marrying her penniless asylum doctor right away? I felt Flo was saying now – "Don't do what I did. Do what I ought to have done. Seize your chance!"

And in the morning, I discovered my mind was made up.

I thought the first person I needed to speak to was Peter Gosforth. It all depended on him really. I rang the *Daily Sketch* office from my telephone box and asked to be put through, saying it was about Hugh O'Donnell. I told him my idea and waited for him to say it was absolutely out of the question, but after a couple of minutes' silence, he said,

"Do you know, I think you might have something there! Leave it with me."

I said, "I don't want to get you into trouble with the Foreign Office."

"Sod the Foreign Office! I want my cartoonist back!"

Then I went round to Maria's studio to confess. I was following her into her kitchen as I told her and she actually did a double take. I never saw anyone do that before. She looked very worried about it but didn't actually explode as I had feared.

Thursday 12ᵗʰ October 1972

Maria arrived at my place at 8 a.m. I haven't been getting to sleep until about 6 in the morning, and I was still in my pyjamas and somewhat bleary eyed. She bounced in, flapping a copy of the *Daily Sketch* in my face.

"He's done it!"

And there it was on the front page – a big photo of Hugh and a write up describing how he had given up his chance of release to Adika, and inviting people to write in to the paper in his support. The address was a PO Box in Hereford. Maria says the letters (if we get any) are coming to the main post office here for us to deal with. We looked at each other wide eyed.

"What have we done?" I asked.

"What have YOU done?" she replied, grinning.

Oh, if only it works!

Friday 13ᵗʰ October 1972

The feeling of actually doing something made me feel so much better that I decided to go into work after Maria left. Giles showed me today's copy of the *Daily Sketch* Hugh's picture and blurb is in there again, though not on the front page. Giles was almost as excited as I was. I don't believe he can really be in love with me or he wouldn't be so keen to get Hugh back.

21 letters collected from the post office today! Marie and I went to get them together before closing time. Some of them just say, PLEASE RELEASE HUGH O'DONNELL! But others say how much they enjoy his cartoons, and one woman said she chose which of her boyfriends to marry by seeing which one laughed most at Klambi. Sounds a bit of a risky foundation for marriage.

21 letters aren't going to get Hugh out of prison, I don't think, but it's a start.

Saturday 14th October 1972

Today the man behind the counter gave me a big grin when I went in.

"How are your muscles?" he asked.

There was a great big sack full of letters asking for Hugh's release! I took them round to Maria's and we spent the whole evening opening them up and reading them. There were 758 letters!

It's so lovely that people care enough to write.

I wonder if that's the most we shall get. Perhaps it will start tailing off a bit now. 779 letters. If we could just get to the thousand.

Sunday 15th October 1972

Sunday. No post. Curses! I took my mind off things by cycling over to Gwen's to see how Jenny is getting along in her new job. I was surprised to find Giles there. It came to me on the way home that it would be a good thing if Giles were to marry Jenny, but it'll never happen. Jenny doesn't seem to like him at all. When I got there, they were having a heated argument about the situation in Ireland.

I can't wait for tomorrow's post. Mum and Dad are back. I went over to update them on the latest. I took the newspaper over to show them. We talked and talked about it. They said if we get enough names on the petition (Maria and I are transferring onto the petition all the names of the people who have written in) they would like to come with us to hand it in. That would be great!

The day went quite quickly in the end, but I can't wait for tomorrow's post.

Monday 16th October 1972

This is incredible! Four big sacks! Maria's flat is drowning in paper so I have asked Alison if we can keep the letters in the room above the shop, where we have the CCC sessions. She said that would be fine. She said as I obviously hadn't had time to think of any sewing projects for the CCC, perhaps they might like to come along and help open the letters – specially as it was Serena's idea.

I hadn't even thought of letting poor Serena know what has been happening. All I can think about at the moment is Hugh.

Tuesday 17th October 1972

The present tally is 9,347 signatures on our petition!

All the CCC members turned out to help this evening. Maria said she didn't know how we would have coped without them, and would they all like to join us in presenting the petition at No 10?

They're all coming! Felicity's Dad came along to help too, this evening, and it turns out he runs a minibus service and can take us all to London. People are just so kind!

We decided that we would go up to Downing Street with the petition this Saturday. There may be more letters to come but neither Maria nor I can bear the thought of Hugh being in prison a minute longer than he has to.

Peter has promised to get some television coverage.

How I wish Hugh could read some of these letters! There was one man who said he and his wife used to look for Klambi in the paper together every day. After she died, he went on doing it and he felt that that was the time when she seemed very close to him. He wanted to thank Hugh.

Hugh and Klambi have touched so many people's lives.

Friday 20th October 1972

I have been too exhausted to write my diary over the last few days. Giles and Gwen and Jenny and Mum and Dad and Rob have all helped in collecting and opening the letters. And Vanessa turned up today with Alice to give us a hand! I was really touched.

We have – wait for it – 23,651 letters!!!!!!

The petition is somewhat longer than anticipated!

Tomorrow is the day. Felicity's Dad is collecting us all from outside Alison's shop at 8.30 a.m.

I can't help feeling if this doesn't work, then we're done for. I'm so scared.

Saturday 21st October 1972

Well, we did it! We gave our petition to Mr Heath. He looked just like he does on the news – lots of teeth and rather flushed. He was very charming and polite and strangely, a little shy. Thanked us and said he would do what he could. It took about five minutes and there was hardly anyone about, but the TV cameras were there filming us handing the petition over, and after the door of No 10 had shut, they interviewed Maria with the rest of us standing around her. Serena had a big placard with a picture of an elephant and "SAVE OUR KLAMBI!" on it. Felicity was holding her elephant.

I am staying with Mum and Dad tonight. They thought I might need company. We watched ourselves on the evening news. I thought – finally, someone is taking notice. This MUST make a difference. But now everything seems an anti-climax and I feel quite despairing of it making any difference at all.

Or worse – suppose I have made a complete mess of things and what I have done cancels out any chance of Hugh getting out?

Monday 23rd October 1972

Yesterday was a bit of a blur, I woke up with a tremendous headache and stayed in bed all day. It was nice being cosseted by Mum. She wasn't there very much during my childhood and school matrons really aren't the same.

There has been absolutely no response from the Foreign Office.

Wednesday 25th October 1972

We've done it! They are releasing him the day after tomorrow! Maria rang me at work this morning to let me know she had had that message from Nick Mason at the Foreign Office. No explanation. Just that.

I am writing to all our CCC members to thank them. I want to thank everyone in the world.

9th November 1972

Dear Gwen

I am writing this sitting at a window looking out across the sea to the Isle of Arran. The air is still and the sea is softly wrinkling like jam does when you are checking to see if it is set. The sea and the sky are very nearly the same pale lavender colour. If it weren't for the slightly darker lavender hills of Arran between the two, you couldn't see where one starts and the other begins. That's rather like how it is between Hugh and me – the dark hills being Hugh's memories of prison which lie between us. I can't wait for them to fade away so that things can be as they were, but I worry that they will be there, between us, for ever.

I was so happy when I saw him walking down the steps from the plane. Then, waiting for the door to open, I was suddenly terrified. I didn't know what to say to him or how to react. He came in with Nick Mason behind him, stopped suddenly when he saw Maria and myself in the room, gave a big smile and opened his arms to hug both of us at once. Being able to touch him again was wonderful. I felt as if I had come home. But he was so thin, and he looked rather biblical with his hair not having been cut for months. He was wearing a suit they must have given him at the Embassy. I don't think I'd ever seen him in a suit before! It sounds awful but I was afraid as we were waiting that he might smell of prison. He didn't.

Adika and his wife, Sarah, had come with us. It was so touching to see Adika and Hugh reunited. They didn't say anything at first, just shook hands, and Hugh made some comment which was obviously a joke between them because Adika laughed and then they hugged each other. Adika told us he and Sarah are going to be allowed to settle in Hereford near Kartika.

I'm sorry I didn't have time to say goodbye before we left Hereford. Everything happened so quickly.

The owners of the *Daily Sketch* were grateful to him for all the publicity they got through the campaign and, after consulting Maria, they arranged for Hugh and myself to stay in this little cottage on the Mull of Kintyre. We flew in a private plane directly from RAF Fairford to Campbeltown. We felt like secret agents landing in the MOD airfield. Apparently, the Americans keep nuclear weapons there. I could almost see Giles' wife, Susan, marching up and down outside with a placard. You can't imagine war or violence on this beautiful, almost-island, though. The only sound in our little cottage is the crackling of logs on the fire and – occasionally – the thump and splash of waves on the pebbles. The sea is about 50 yards away. I sit in the porch early in the morning and watch for otters while Hugh is still asleep.

At first, all Hugh could think about was contacting Amnesty International and trying to help in some way to improve conditions for the prisoners in Salemba. He has written a long report and sent it to them. I hated watching him doing it because he was obviously reliving it all. Having done it, he seems a bit more peaceful. He still gets nightmares but I'm hoping that that is helping him to sort it all out on a subconscious level somehow.

I feel very inadequate sometimes, but I remember what you said about being patient and not expecting things to go back as they were right away. He never used to be irritated with me ever, but now he is and afterwards he is so apologetic. I could cry.

Physically, he is gaining weight and doesn't seem to be any the worse for having been six months in prison on an awful diet.

There are times when he tells me of funny little things that happened in prison, and that is a huge relief to me – that there were times when it wasn't too horrible. And gradually, he is telling me the sad things too, which must be good for him.

To begin with, he slept and slept. The cottage is quite on its own and there are no lights except the stars. If you wake up in the night and have to go to the bathroom, it is so completely black that you can't see a thing. He says after six months of sleeping with the light on, it's wonderful to sleep in the dark again.

Now he is sleeping less and we walk for miles, often not saying anything at all. It is the loveliest place. There are miles of beaches – you can just keep going forever – sometimes pebbles, sometimes sand. There are herons and gulls and oyster catchers, and every so often you hear the haunting cry of a curlew. We haven't seen an otter yet, but we keep looking.

I know that deep down there is still this link between us which hasn't been broken, but can we ever get back to how things were? I don't know.

With lots of love

Jane

PS Great news about Jenny. Tell her not to have the wedding until I can get there.

PPS Did you hear about Mrs Suharto? Maria's contact at the Foreign Office told us (unofficially) that the reason they let Hugh go in the end was that President Suharto's wife likes to read the English newspapers and she loves Klambi in the *Daily Sketch*. She saw the campaign to get Hugh back and the picture of Mr Heath taking our petition on the steps of No 10, and told her husband to sort it! You were right about individuals succeeding where organisations fail!

Rhyd-Ddu
Caernarvon
Wales

18th March 1973

Dear Bernadette

It was good to hear that you arrived safely back home in Ireland. It was great to have you here. You must come again. Never be thinking you are in the way. Jane loved having you with us, and in her present state, she was glad to have you taking over the kitchen in the mornings. The breakfasts I was cooking before you arrived were nothing to tempt her with, even if she had been able to think about food.

I was so happy to read what you wrote about her in your letter. She's the dearest girl that ever was. But you would not be believing the change in her since I left for Java! When I first knew her it was I who led and she followed. Now it's the other way around. I swear to you – I am the most henpecked of husbands!

I wondered whether she would understand that Maria would always be a part of my life. I need not have worried. She asks me now, "Have you rung Maria this week?" I tell her – "Sure, 'tis a terrible scold of a woman I have married!" I like to hear Jane and Maria arguing over "The Invisible Elephant Company". Jane takes on board most of the good advice Maria gives her but there is a certain point beyond which she will not be pushed. I wouldn't give Jane advice, even if I had any to give. It's her venture. All I've done is to give her the Klambi logo. I like to think that our elephants are intertwined, just as we are.

I ask Jane if she would be happier back in Hereford, keeping an eye on the company, but she says she is happy here. Once I used to yearn to be off exploring the world, while she would be the one to be at home. Now she says if I get the wanderlust upon me again, she will be happy to come with me. At present, though, I am glad to stay at home in our little grey cottage and watch the rain fall.

While I was away, she found herself, and every day she gives that self to me, your worthless little brother. I am the luckiest man that ever lived.

With much love to you and the Old Country.

Hugh

24th October 1973

Dear Gwen

Well, here they are! I took the photo while kneeling on top of the garden wall, so it's a bit wobbly. Patrick is just as beautiful as Audrey really – it's just that the sun was in his eyes. Their full names are – Patrick Robert William O'Donnell and Audrey Bridget Florence O'Donnell. I know – they are going to curse us when they get to school, aren't they? But we had to have both our mothers and fathers in there – and you will know the reason for the names William and Florence. I wanted dear Mac and Flo to be part of our happiness.

We had absolutely no idea that I was having twins and Hugh had to rush out and get one more of everything. My mother is in her element – she seems to have suddenly developed a maternal side! Dad and Rob are looking forward to taking them up mountains when they are big enough to put on climbing boots. Snowdon is just up the road from our little cottage so it's handy. I'm glad we moved here. The publicity wasn't good for Hugh in Hereford.

Did you see on the news that he recently donated a special Klambi cartoon for an Amnesty International charity auction? They raised over £6,000 with it. Isn't that brilliant?

You should see how many drawings he has done of the twins. He spends hours just watching their faces. For an antique Dad, he is very modern – he even changes their nappies! Just as well, because the minute you finish changing one, you have to start on the other. I can't tell you how lovely it is to have the old Hugh back. I seem to spend my days laughing. Sometimes I get scared about being so happy – I have too much to lose.

"The Invisible Elephant Company" is doing well. Kartika is a born manager and tactfully keeps Serena in check. Dear Serena! I can never forget that it was her idea of a campaign which brought my Hugh home. The elephants have become a bit of a cult in Hereford for some reason. I'm thinking of branching out. Hugh suggests mice. He says, look how well that Robert Thompson did with them. I tell him I couldn't possibly scare my poor elephants with mice.

Jenny wrote to say she and Giles have been deeply involved with the "Hands off Herefordshire" campaign. They took a Herefordshire bull to London in protest! Giles' Susan would have been proud of him! Jenny says they argue as much as ever! There was a little note from Alice at the bottom of Jenny's letter, asking me to make an elephant for baby Jonathan.

I've been asked if I would write a book about Hugh and how I coped while he was in prison, and the campaign and everything. It's all much too personal. I know who I would like to write a book about, and that's Mac and Flo. I think I might.

Take care. Come and visit us SOON!

Much love

Jane